# Connectivity
LEVEL 2

CONNECTING PEOPLE THROUGH ENGLISH

WORKBOOK

Joan Saslow
Allen Ascher

Connectivity 2
Workbook

Copyright © 2022 by Pearson Education, Inc.

All rights reserved.

No part of this publication may be reproduced, stored in a retrieval system, or transmitted in any form or by any means, electronic, mechanical, photocopying, recording, or otherwise, without the prior permission of the publisher.

Pearson Education, 221 River Street, Hoboken, NJ 07030 USA

Text composition: ElectraGraphics, Inc.

Photo Credits:

Unit 1
Page 3 (1): Sabphoto/Shutterstock; 3 (2): New Africa/Shutterstock; 3 (3): Morrowind/Shutterstock; 3 (4): I_am_zews/Shutterstock; 3 (5): Sam Wordley/Shutterstock; 3 (6): Fizkes/Shutterstock; 3 (7): RDaniel/Shutterstock; 5 (1): VladimirGjorgiev/123RF; 5 (2): Pathdoc/Shutterstock; 5 (3): TakeAPixMedia/Shutterstock; 5 (4): Stuart Monk/Shutterstock; 5 (bottom): Grafner/123RF; 7: Yurumi/Shutterstock; 8: Mimagephotography/123RF.

Unit 2
Page 13: Cynoclub/Shutterstock; 14: Songquan Deng/Shutterstock; 15: Wissutaon/Shutterstock; 16 (1): Wavebreakmedia/Shutterstock; 16 (2): Peter Bernik/Shutterstock; 16 (3): Sonmueng/123RF; 16 (4): Dean Drobot/123RF; 16 (5): Stylephotographs/123RF; 16 (6): StockerThai-Esarn/Shutterstock; 17: ESB Basic/Shutterstock.

Unit 3
Page 26: Sdecoret/Shutterstock.

Unit 4
Page 30 (1): AboutLife/Shutterstock; 30 (2): FotoluminateLLC/Shutterstock; 30 (3): Rohappy/Shutterstock; 30 (4): G-stockstudio/Shutterstock; 30 (5): DaxiaoProductions/Shutterstock; 30 (6): Jami Garrison/Shutterstock; 32 (1): Edvard Nalbantjan/Shutterstock; 32 (2): Sarymsakov Andrey/Shutterstock; 32 (3): Rjlerich/Shutterstock; 32 (4): Ljupco Smokovski/Shutterstock; 32 (5): Natalya Erofeeva/Shutterstock; 32 (6): 3DMI/Shutterstock; 32 (7): Dima Moroz/Shutterstock; 34 (1): Miljan Zivkovic/Shutterstock; 34 (2): Feng Yu/Shutterstock; 34 (3): Avirut S/Shutterstock; 34 (4): Andrey_Popov/Shutterstock; 34 (5): Lunopark/Shutterstock; 34 (6): Kzenon/123RF; 35: Rob Wilson/Shutterstock.

Unit 5
Page 41 (1): UfaBizPhoto/Shutterstock; 41 (2): Tomek_Pa/Shutterstock; 41 (3): Gemenacom/Shutterstock; 41 (4): Basyn/Shutterstock; 41 (5): Jean-Paul/123RF; 41 (6): New Africa/Shutterstock; 43 (1): Mudvayne/Shutterestock; 43 (2): Alona Siniehina/Shutterstock; 43 (3): HalitOmer/Shutterstock; 43 (4): Peter Bernik/Shutterstock; 43 (5): AtelierKNOX/Shutterstock; 43 (6): Ahmet Naim/Shutterstock; 43 (7): Microgen/Shutterstock; 44: Dmitry Kalinovsky/123RF.

Library of Congress Cataloging-in-Publication Data

A catalog record for the print edition is available from the Library of Congress

Printed in the United States of America
ISBN-13: 978-0-13-683446-5
1 2021

pearsonenglish.com/connectivity

Unit 6

Page 48 (1): Kurhan/Shutterstock; 48 (2 inset): Simply Amazing/Shutterstock; 48 (2): Dndavis/123RF; 48 (3): Shisu_ka/Shutterstock; 48 (4): Kosmos111/Shutterstock; 48 (5): Anton Estrada/123RF; 48 (6): Prostock-studio/Shutterstock; 50: Natu/Shutterstock; 52: Barmalini/Shutterstock; 53: Sandra Sneekes-Pacque/Shutterstock; 54: Fotosutra/Shutterstock.

Unit 7

Page 57 (2): Flat vectors/Shutterstock; 57 (4): TatyanaKar/Shutterstock; 57 (7): Robuart/Shutterstock; 57 (8): Lucien Fraud/Shutterstock; Page 58 (1): Nor Gal/Shutterstock; 58 (2): Lena Pan/Shutterstock; 58 (3): Macrovector/Shutterstock; 58 (4): Ensuper/Shutterstock; 60 (1): PongMoji/Shutterstock; 60 (2): KonstantinosMoraitis/123RF; 60 (3): Freedomz/Shutterstock; 60 (4): Kwangmoozaa/Shutterstock; 60 (5): Vpvhunter/Shutterstock; 60 (6): Robert Crum/Shutterstock; 62 (1): Jinga/Shutterstock; 62 (2): Nikola Barbutov/Shutterstock; 62 (3): Sergei Butorin/Shutterstock; 62 (4): Lopolo/Shutterstock; 62 (5): Macrovector/Shutterstock; 62 (6): Arda savasciogullari/Shutterstock; 62 (7): Tommaso Altamura/123RF; 63 (1): Nestor Rizhniak/Shutterstock; 63 (2): Mandy Godbehear/Shutterstock; 63 (3): Baloncici/Shutterstock.

Unit 8

Page 67 (a): R Ashrafov/Shutterstock; 67 (b): 3445128471/Shutterstock; 67 (c): EvgeniiAnd/Shutterstock; 67 (d): Voyagerix/Shutterstock; 67 (e): R.classen/Shutterstock; 67 (f): Cunaplus/123RF; 67 (g): Stuart Cox/PearsonEducationLtd; 71 (1): Zkruger/Shutterstock; 71 (2): Wavebreakmedia/Shutterstock; 71 (3): ConstantinePankin/123RF; 71 (4): Michal Kowalski/Shutterstock; 72: Karenroach/Shutterstock.

Unit 9

Page 75 (1): Karakotsya/Shutterstock; 75 (2): Agsandrew/Shutterstock; 75 (3): Paul prescott/Shutterstock; 75 (4): Seaskylab/Shutterstock; 75 (5): Everett Collection/Shutterstock; 75 (6): Little_larc/Shutterstock; 77 (1,1): Chempina/Shutterstock; 77 (1,2): Africa Studio/Shutterstock; 77 (1,3): Dario Lo Presti/Shutterstock; 77 (1,4): Deborah McCague/Shutterstock; 77 (1,5): Mayabuns/Shutterstock; 77 (1,6): Pavel K/Shutterstock; 77 (2,1 left): Isak 55/Shutterstock; 77 (2,1 center): Kavee Vivii/Shutterstock; 77 (2,1 right): Stockphoto mania/Shutterstock; 77 (2,2left): NJHPhotography/Shutterstock; 77 (2,2 center): Antonio Veraldi/123RF; 77 (2,2 right): Solomin Andrey/123RF; 77 (2,3 left): Alexandra Karamysheva/123RF; 77 (2,3 center): Paichuu/Shutterstock; 77 (2,3 right): Viktoriya Chursina/123RF; 77 (2,4 left): Dario Sabljak/Shutterstock; 77 (2,4 center): Sopotnicki/Shutterstock; 77 (2,4 right): Buteo/Shutterstock; 79: Bbtreesubmission/123RF; 80: Alexander Pokusay/123RF; 81: Chepurko Ekaterina/Shutterstock.

Unit 10

Page 88 (left): Aleksanderdn/123RF; 88 (right): Valeriy Lebedev/Shutterstock; 89 (1): Fizkes/Shutterstock; 89 (2): Ventdusud/Shutterstock; 89 (3): Shutterstock; 89 (4): TakeAPixMedia/Shutterstock; 89 (5): CathyYeulet/123RF; 90: Tashatuvango/123RF.

Illustration Credits

Steve Attoe pp. 11, 18, 29, 47, 68 (top); Leeanne Franson pp. 60, 68 (bottom 2); Brian Hughes p. 41 (left 2, right 2); Stephen Hutchings p. 31; Andy Myer p. 21 (1, 2); Dusan Petricic p. 36; Joe Sarver p. 41 (center); Geoffrey P. Smith p. 57 (1, 3, 5, 6, 8); Anne Veltfort pp. 21 (3, 4), 42.

CONTENTS

UNIT 1	Making New Friends	1
UNIT 2	Sharing Life Experiences	11
UNIT 3	Talking about Movies	20
UNIT 4	Away from Home	29
UNIT 5	Looking Good	38
UNIT 6	Eating Well	47
UNIT 7	Driving Around	57
UNIT 8	Doing the Right Thing	66
UNIT 9	Enjoying the Arts	75
UNIT 10	Technology	84

UNIT 1 Making New Friends

Warm-up

1 Read the posts on an online message board. Rank the people from 1 to 5 with 1 being the most introverted and 5 being the most extroverted.

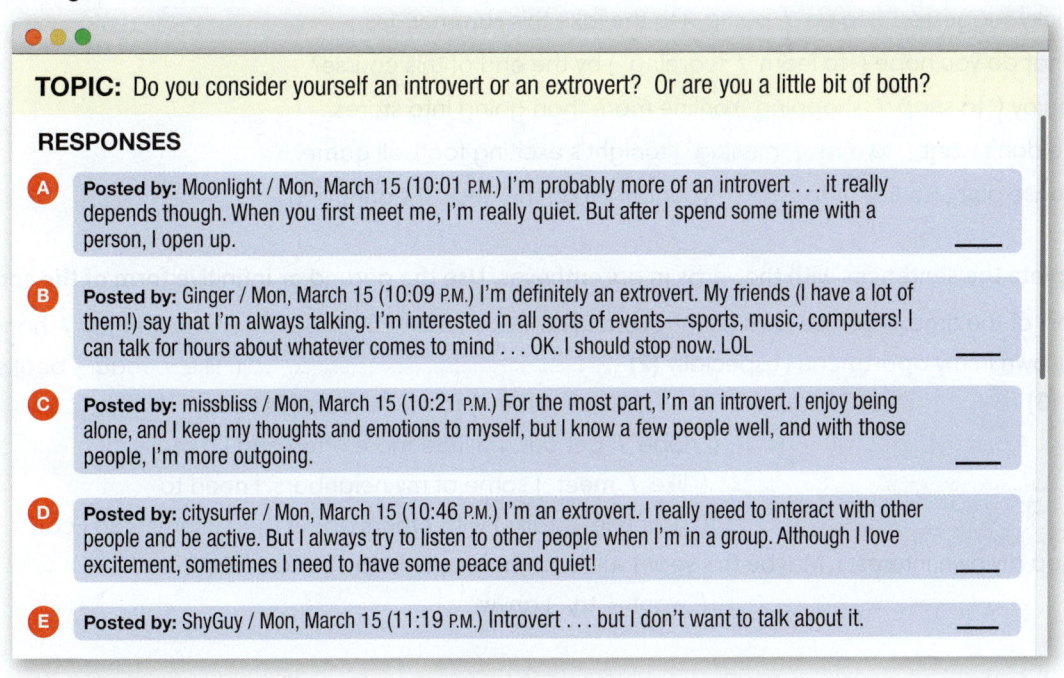

TOPIC: Do you consider yourself an introvert or an extrovert? Or are you a little bit of both?

RESPONSES

A Posted by: Moonlight / Mon, March 15 (10:01 P.M.) I'm probably more of an introvert . . . it really depends though. When you first meet me, I'm really quiet. But after I spend some time with a person, I open up. ____

B Posted by: Ginger / Mon, March 15 (10:09 P.M.) I'm definitely an extrovert. My friends (I have a lot of them!) say that I'm always talking. I'm interested in all sorts of events—sports, music, computers! I can talk for hours about whatever comes to mind . . . OK. I should stop now. LOL ____

C Posted by: missbliss / Mon, March 15 (10:21 P.M.) For the most part, I'm an introvert. I enjoy being alone, and I keep my thoughts and emotions to myself, but I know a few people well, and with those people, I'm more outgoing. ____

D Posted by: citysurfer / Mon, March 15 (10:46 P.M.) I'm an extrovert. I really need to interact with other people and be active. But I always try to listen to other people when I'm in a group. Although I love excitement, sometimes I need to have some peace and quiet! ____

E Posted by: ShyGuy / Mon, March 15 (11:19 P.M.) Introvert . . . but I don't want to talk about it. ____

2 Are you an introvert, an extrovert, or a little bit of both? Write your own reply.

Posted by: _____

_____
_____

3 Match each phrase with its meaning. Draw a line.

1 What's up?
2 It's pretty short notice.
3 Two heads are better than one.
4 I thank my lucky stars for that.
5 I'm feeling a little blue.
6 Are you getting along?

a It's easier to solve problems together.
b I'm grateful for or happy with it.
c I'm unhappy or feeling down.
d That's not a lot of time to decide.
e Is everything OK in your relationship?
f Is anything wrong?

LESSON 1

1 Circle the correct form of the verb to complete each sentence.

1 We're going to start (to exercise / **exercising**) in the mornings before work.
2 She wants (**to ride** / riding) her new bike on a trail this weekend.
3 He plans (**to finish** / finishing) his latest project by the end of the week.
4 Meredith is interested in (to take / **taking**) a cooking class with you.
5 My family loves (to watch / **watching**) animated movies together.
6 Micky suggested (to go / **going**) to the lake this summer.
7 What do you hope (**to learn** / learning) by the end of this course?
8 I enjoy (to shop / **shopping**) online more than going into stores.
9 We don't want (**to miss** / missing) tonight's exciting football game.
10 Please quit (to tap / **tapping**) your pencil on the desk. It's annoying.

2 Complete the sentences with the verbs in parentheses. Use the gerund or infinitive form of the second verb.

Most of the time, I feel like I am an introvert. I (1) _enjoy hanging out_ (enjoy / hang out) on my own in my apartment. I especially (2) .... (like / read) books and I (3) .... (like / listen) to music. But, this year, I (4) .... (hope / get out) a little more often and I'd really (5) .... (like / meet) some of my neighbors. I need to (6) .... (practice / talk) with others about their interests so I can develop my own interests. Maybe this year I will learn how easy it can be to make friends. I (7) .... (want / try) anyway.

3 Complete the conversation with the correct words from the box. You will not use all the words.

| about you | baking | chores | fiction books | hobbies | in common | other interests | washing |

A: So tell me about yourself.
B: Sure! What would you like to know?
A: Well, for example, do you have any (1) ....?
B: Hobbies? Not really.
A: What about (2) ....?
B: Well, I like (3) .... cookies and reading (4) ....
A: Me too! And is there anything you definitely don't enjoy?
B: Let me think . . . Oh, yeah! I really don't like (5) .... dishes.
A: Me neither! What a coincidence! We have a lot (6) ....

4 Think about your hobbies and other interests. Do you and your best friend have the same likes and dislikes? Complete the chart.

Hobbies	You	Your friend
exercise	like	dislike

5 Review the information from the chart in Exercise 4. Write four sentences about you and your friend's hobbies and interests. Use gerunds and infinitives.

1 I enjoy exercising but my best friend can't stand to exercise.
2 ....
3 ....
4 ....
5 ....

LESSON 2

1 Look at each picture. Circle the correct adjective + preposition.

1 He's (crazy about / angry about / bored with) his homework.

2 She's (sick and tired of / afraid of / crazy about) strawberry ice cream.

3 Tracey is (excited about / afraid of / angry about) the dark.

4 They're (excited about / upset about / bored with) the new music video.

5 She's (afraid of / angry about / sick and tired of) eating vegetables every day.

6 Clayton is (upset about / crazy about / excited about) the latest e-mail from his colleague.

7 Aleyda is (angry about / excited about / bored with) her broken computer.

UNIT 1

2 Complete the sentences with the correct adjective + preposition from the box.

afraid of   angry about   bored with   crazy about   excited about   sick and tired of   upset about

1 I have a mountain of laundry to do. It never ends. I'm .... doing chores!
2 My cousins went swimming at the lake today. I didn't go. I'm .... the water.
3 I can't believe that car cut me off. So thoughtless. I get so .... bad drivers on the road.
4 We got tickets for the Super Bowl! I can't wait! I'm so .... this game.
5 This movie is really bad. My friend was so .... it, he fell asleep.
6 Armando was .... having to stay late at the office to finish a co-worker's project.
7 You always wear the cutest clothes. I'm absolutely .... your sense of style.

3 Complete the conversation. Use the correct preposition with the verb or adjective, and a gerund.

A: You look blue? What's up?

B: Oh, nothing major. I'm just ....*sick and tired of working*.......... late every night.
   1 sick and tired / work

A: But I thought you liked your job.

B: I do. Well mostly. I guess I'm a little .... the same thing every day. And I
   2 bored / do
   feel .... enough time at home.
   3 unhappy / not spend

A: Have you .... your schedule with your boss?
   4 talk / change

B: No. I'm .... her angry.
   5 afraid / make

A: What about talking with your coworkers? Maybe they can give you some advice.

B: That's a good idea. I'll .... that this week.
   6 think / do

4 Complete the conversations. Write the preposition and circle the correct form of the verb.

1 A: What's the matter with Jack?
   B: Oh, he's angry ....*about*.......... (lose / (losing)) his tennis match.

2 A: Don't you think working out before going into the office is best?
   B: Yes, but Mike objects .... (getting up / get up) at 4:00 in the morning.

3 A: What do you think about Jessy's presentation?
   B: Well, I like that she believes .... (to speak / speaking) her mind.

4 A: Why has Karl been so blue lately?
   B: He told me that he's sick and tired .... (working / work) so many hours.

5 A: I'm so busy this weekend, but I'm not really crazy .... (look / looking) at these horrible nails much longer.
   B: So, let's go to the salon at lunch time.

6 A: Aren't you excited .... (trying / tries) out the new restaurant this weekend?
   B: Yes, I am. I can't wait!

7 A: Let's do something different tonight.
   B: I agree. I'm bored .... (go / going) to the same clubs all the time.

5 Complete the conversation with words from the box.

| I'm so sorry | It's nothing serious | sick and tired of |
| That might cheer you up | That's a great idea | You look down |

A: Hey, June, what's up? **(1)** ....

B: Just some minor problems at work. Thanks for asking. **(2)** ....

A: Are you sure?

B: Well, actually, I'm **(3)** .... working so many hours. I'm thinking of looking for a new job.

A: **(4)** .... Is there anything I can do?

B: Probably not, but I appreciate your concern.

A: Well, how about getting together to see a movie sometime? **(5)** ....

B: **(6)** .... ! How about this weekend?

6 Read about how the people are feeling. Suggest something to cheer them up. Write complete sentences.

> I'm sick and tired of this job. I've been working late every night for a month!

> I'm really upset that I didn't get a raise at work. I've been struggling this year.

1 ....

2 ....

> I've been feeling blue lately. I think I'm just bored with everyday life.

> A rainy day always puts me in a bad mood.

3 ....

4 ....

DID YOU KNOW . . . ?

Food to Improve Your Mood
Studies show that eating certain foods can help cheer you up when you are feeling blue. Eating foods that contain vitamins D and B and omega-3 fatty acids, such as fish, nuts, eggs, spinach, and bananas, increase the chemicals in your brain that make you feel happy and relaxed.

LESSON 3

1 Read the article. According to astrology, what force can change human psychology and events? Circle the correct letter.

a the genes we get from our parents

b the sun, stars, and our birthdate

c the environment we grow up in

ASTROLOGY—Finding Your Personality in the Stars

Why do you act the way you do? What is the secret to your emotions, or your moods or feelings? Where does your personality, or the characteristics that make you *you*, come from? Is it nature or nurture? In other words, is it something you are born with or is it something that you learn as you grow up? Is it affected by genetics (genes you inherited from your parents) or the environment (the world you live in)? Or could it be the sun and the stars?

Some people think that birth order influences personality, while many others believe that the day on which you were born influences your personality. These people believe in astrology—the study of the movements and positions of celestial (positioned in the sky) bodies and how they might influence human affairs. They believe that the sun and the stars influence human personality and events.

Astrology may be a way to understand human personality. Or it may be a false science. But millions of people around the world read their astrological horoscope (a brief forecast for people born at a certain time of the year or under a particular sign) every day—just in case! See below for examples of personality traits attributed to each of the astrology signs, also called zodiac signs.

Aquarius ♒
Jan 20–Feb 18
- very active
- cheerful
- can be a clown

Gemini ♊
May 21–Jun 21
- worries about things
- can be self-critical
- can be hard to know

Libra ♎
Sept 23–Oct 23
- conservative
- spends time with a few friends
- has strong emotions

Pisces ♓
Feb 19–Mar 20
- honest
- easily bored with jobs
- likes quiet time

Cancer ♋
Jun 22–Jul 22
- interested in travel
- enjoys being with other people
- always behaves appropriately

Scorpio ♏
Oct 24–Nov 21
- friendly
- sensitive to others' emotions
- not easy to get to know

Aries ♈
Mar 21–Apr 19
- enjoys being alone
- hard to get to know
- keeps thoughts and emotions inside

Leo ♌
Jul 23–Aug 22
- happy with lots of people
- cheers people up
- crazy about nature

Sagittarius ♐
Nov 22–Dec 21
- creative
- likes everything in moderation
- gets along with everyone

Taurus ♉
Mar 21–Apr 19
- calm
- seeks peace
- good listener

Virgo ♍
Aug 23–Sept 22
- keeps ideas inside
- likes to spend time alone
- enjoys reading

Capricorn ♑
Dec 22–Jan 19
- has a lot of friends
- interested in events
- loves excitement

2 Answer the questions according to the article in Exercise 1.

1 Which of the zodiac signs describe more of an introvert? ....
....

2 Which signs describe more of an extrovert? ....
....

3 Which sign describes people who might enjoy traveling to foreign countries on vacation?
....

4 Which sign describes someone who might enjoy painting and writing books? ....

5 What zodiac sign are you? .... Does the description for your sign describe you accurately? Why or why not? ....
....

6 Compare the personality traits for your birth order (as described on p. 8 in the Student Book) with the personality traits for your zodiac sign. Are there any similarities? Which describes you better?
....
....
....
....

3 Complete each statement with the correct word from the box. You will not use two of the words.

| astrology | born | characteristics | emotions | genetics | nurture | personality | stars | zodiac |

1 Your personality is the .... that make you who you are.

2 Some people think personality is something you were .... with.

3 Others think personality can be inherited from your parents through ....

4 People who believe in .... believe the day on which you were born influences your personality.

5 They say the position of the sun and the .... influence personality and events.

6 Some people think that birth order also influences your ....

7 Examples of personality traits are attributed to each of the .... signs.

UNIT 1   7

LESSON 4

1 Match the kinds of friends on the left with the definitions on the right. Draw a line.

1 an acquaintance
2 a close friend
3 a best friend
4 a fair-weather friend
5 a family friend
6 a social-media friend
7 a soul mate

a a person who is your friend in good times only
b a special person who you love and who likes and believes the same things as you do
c a person who is friends with your parents or siblings
d a person you just met or someone you don't know very well
e a good friend who supports, understands, and listens to you
f a person who you communicate with online rather than in person
g of all your friends, this is the one that you are closest to

2 Read each description. What kind of friend is it? Circle the correct answer.

1 Shelly and I became friends when we were only 5 years old. We talk every week even if we can't meet in person. I share all my secrets with her because I know she won't tell anyone.
   a a best friend
   b an acquaintance
   c a social-media friend

2 Kevin, Noah, and I have worked together for a few years. When I have problems, I know I can talk to them. They always listen and try to help me. I think we'll always be friends.
   a social-media friends
   b family friends
   c close friends

3 We don't know Alison very well. We just met her at a conference.
   a a best friend
   b an acquaintance
   c a family friend

4 Angelica met Dawn through a Facebook Mom's group. They live in different states, but they message each other fairly often.
   a a social media friend
   b a best friend
   c an acquaintance

5 I'm so happy I introduced Ryan and Rhonda. They like the same things. They laugh at the same jokes. They even dress alike. They are perfect for each other.
   a close friends
   b soul mates
   c fair-weather friends

6 My father's friend Ben was around a lot when I was growing up. He was always good to us. He and my Dad are still very close. Since he lives alone, I call to check on him once in a while.
   a a family friend
   b an acquaintance
   c a fair-weather friend

7 Whenever we have a party, our neighbors Todd and Trudy always seem to show up in time for the food. But they disappear when it's time to clean up.
   a close friends
   b fair-weather friends
   c soul mates

DID YOU KNOW . . . ?
Recent surveys show that the average person has 4.3 best friends, 7.2 close friends, and 20.4 acquaintances.

GRAMMAR EXPANDER

1 Complete each sentence with a gerund. Use verbs from the box.

attend   drive   get   mow   order   play   run   write

1 On Sundays, we enjoy .... through the countryside.
2 Let's go .... a few mornings a week before work.
3 My daughter is .... her driving permit tomorrow.
4 Hey, we're .... pizza for lunch. Do you want some?
5 You can't go to the mall until you're done .... the lawn.
6 Our whole team is .... the conference next month.
7 Which teams are .... at the stadium on Friday?
8 My son helps me by .... out the grocery list each week.

2 Complete the sentences with your own information. Use the form in parentheses.

1 (gerund as subject) .... is my favorite hobby.
2 (infinitive as subject) .... well is an important skill.
3 (gerund as subject complement) My best friend's hobby is ....
4 (gerund as direct object) I enjoy ....
5 (gerund as object of preposition) I watched a documentary about ....
6 (infinitive as subject complement) My goal is ....
7 (infinitive as direct object) My spouse wants ....

3 Complete each sentence with an affirmative gerund or a negative gerund with <u>not</u>. Use the verbs in parentheses.

1 Kara has been working at home alone for months. She's depressed about .... much time directly with her friends from work. (spend)
2 Health experts suggest .... fewer fatty foods and more vegetables. (eat)
3 How about .... our favorite TV series together tonight? (watch)
4 My energy is low due to .... often enough. (exercise)
5 I'd like to spend the whole day .... in my pajamas. (read)
6 Paul prefers to be .... fiction not reports for his office. (write)
7 Sorry about .... before stopping by. I know how much you dislike unexpected visitors. (call)
8 Ben was worried about .... enough money to pay his bills. (have)
9 You should avoid .... a cell phone while you're driving. (use)
10 Let's start .... I'm going to love .... at that old wallpaper anymore! (paint, look)

WRITING HANDBOOK

1 Complete each sentence. Circle the letter. Use parallel structure. One item has two correct answers.

1 I'm an extrovert. I like .... new people just about anywhere.
   a to meet   b meeting   c meet

2 Keeping ideas inside, spending time alone, and .... reading are traits typical of a Virgo.
   a enjoys   b to enjoy   c enjoying

3 Pisces people tend to be honest, to be easily bored, and .... quiet time.
   a to like   b like   c liking

4 To get to know others better, you should avoid .... too much about yourself and try asking more questions about them.
   a to talk   b talking   c talk

5 He's sick and tired of .... so much, not making enough money, and missing out on time with his family.
   a work   b to work   c working

6 The "baby" or youngest child tends to clown around, ... creative, and to be independent.
   a to be   b is   c being

7 Although he has been seeing a psychologist, he continues to feel down, to avoid interaction with others, and .... all the time.
   a feeling tired   b to feel tired   c feel tired

8 Enjoying being alone, being hard to get to know, and .... and emotions inside are traits typical of an Aries.
   a keeping thoughts   b to keep thoughts   c keep thoughts

9 Some typical behaviors of a middle child are to break rules, have a lot of friends, and .... rebellious.
   a being   b to be   c be

2 Write two paragraphs about your personality. In the first paragraph, tell something about yourself. Use the ideas as a guide. Make sure to use parallel structure. In the second paragraph, discuss where you think your personality traits come from—your parents, birth order, your experiences as a child, or another idea.

I think I'm an extrovert, a rebel, and a clown. I love meeting people, talking, and making people laugh . . .

Ideas
extrovert	self-critical
introvert	hard-working
quiet	creative
active	popular
creative	a rebel
funny	a clown

UNIT 2 Sharing Life Experiences

Warm-up

1 Look at the pictures. Complete the tourist activities.

1 .... Mount Fuji
2 .... New York 
3 .... Korean food 
4 .... the Great Wall 
5 .... the Eiffel Tower 
6 .... the Tower of London 

2 Complete the paragraph with the correct words from the box.

| climb | ride | take a bus tour | takes pictures | tried | walked along | went sightseeing | went to the top of |

Our Trip to Japan

On our first day in Japan, we **(1)** .... Tokyo Tower to enjoy the views of the city. In the evening, we **(2)** .... the busy streets of Shibuya. We saw the famous bright lights and ate delicious street food. Today we **(3)** .... and visited places like Nakamise Shopping Street and the Imperial Palace. We stopped for lunch and **(4)** .... several different Japanese dishes. My husband is a photographer, so he **(5)** .... of every place we visit. Tomorrow we're going to visit Mount Fuji. We aren't in shape, so we're not going to try to **(6)** .... the mountain. Instead, we're going to **(7)** .... We've been told there are many beautiful things to see on the 60 mile (100 kilometer) drive. We also want to **(8)** .... the cable car up Mount Tenjo. It has spectacular views over Lake Kawaguchiko.

3 Match the language that has a similar meaning. Draw a line.

1 You look familiar.
2 I recognize you.
3 If you don't mind my asking, . . .
4 I'd love to show you around.
5 Look me up.

a I'd enjoy taking you on a tour.
b I think I know you from somewhere.
c Contact me later.
d I remember meeting you before.
e Is it OK to ask you . . .

UNIT 2   11

LESSON 1

1 Complete each sentence with the present perfect. Use the words in parentheses. Use contractions when possible.

1. **A:** .... (you / eat) lunch yet today?
   B: Yes, ... (I / have) soup and a salad.
2. **A:** .... (you / read) this author's latest book?
   B: No, I haven't. .... (I / be) too busy.
3. **A:** .... (you / go) to the zoo yet?
   B: Yes, ... (we / be) twice.
4. **A:** .... (he / check in) at the hotel?
   B: No, ... (he / be) delayed.

2 Complete the questions with the correct form of the verbs from the box. Use each verb only once. Then write your own responses. When you answer yes, add specific information, using the simple past tense.

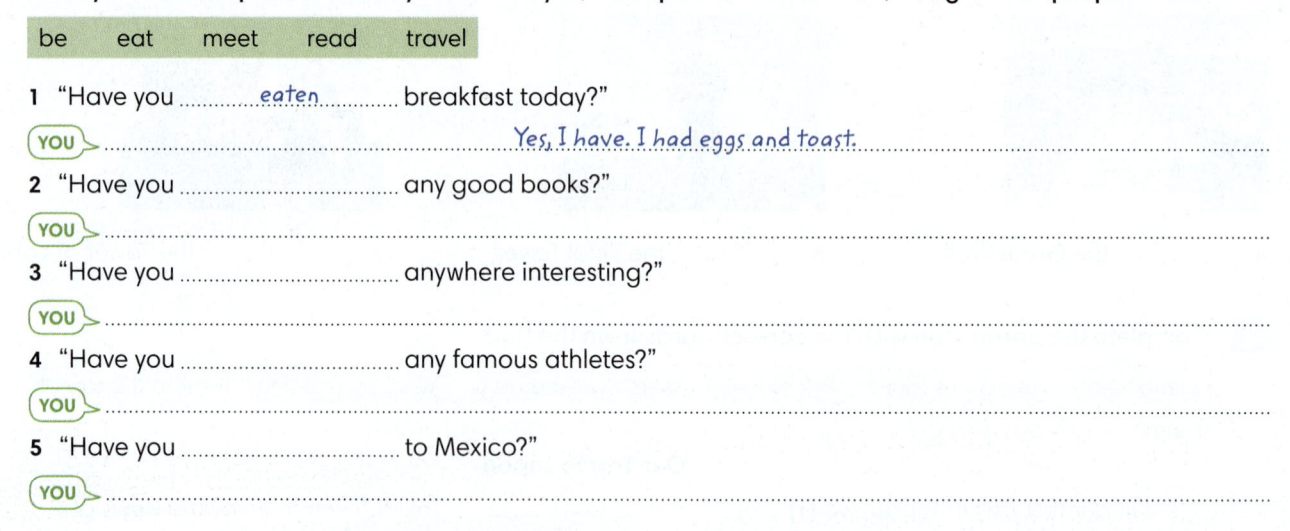

| be   eat   meet   read   travel |

1. "Have you ......*eaten*...... breakfast today?"
   YOU ▸ *Yes, I have. I had eggs and toast.*
2. "Have you .... any good books?"
   YOU ▸ ....
3. "Have you .... anywhere interesting?"
   YOU ▸ ....
4. "Have you .... any famous athletes?"
   YOU ▸ ....
5. "Have you .... to Mexico?"
   YOU ▸ ....

3 Complete the conversation with the present perfect or the simple past tense. Use contractions when possible.

Greta: Hi. I'm Greta. **(1)** .... (you / take) this tour before? I hear it's great.

Rose: I'm Rose. Yes, I have. I **(2)** .... (come) to France with this group three years ago. It **(3)** .... (be) a fantastic trip.
(4) .... (you / be) here before?

Greta: Yes, I **(5)** .... (come) to Paris in 2015, but I only
(6) .... (visit) a few museums. I **(7)** ....
(not / see) much of the city because it **(8)** .... (be) a business trip.
I'm really excited about seeing more things this time!

Rose: Me too. I **(9)** .... (read) through the brochures several times last night. I can't wait to see all these places again and some new ones. By the way,
(10) .... (you / meet) Joseph, our tour guide?

Greta: No, but I'd like to.

Rose: Come on. I'll introduce you.

4 Put the conversation in order. Write the number on the line.

..... **A:** Me? I've been pretty busy with work lately. Plus, I started back at the gym.

_1_ **A:** Adam! It's been a long time! How have you been?

..... **B:** Actually, I've been on vacation. We just got back from Brazil. What about you?

..... **B:** That's great! Listen, I've got to go. But I'd love to catch up some time.

..... **B:** Greg! Great to see you again! I've been fine, thanks. And you?

..... **A:** Absolutely. Let's get together soon.

..... **A:** Not bad. So what have you been up to?

LESSON 2

1 Complete the sentences with words from the box. Three words are used twice.

already   before   ever   never   yet

1. Have you .... been on a train?
2. Which one is your brother? I've .... met him.
3. I haven't ridden a camel .... Have you?
4. We haven't made it to the museum ....
5. Should we go to dinner or have you .... eaten?
6. Have you .... tried calamari?
7. We've .... been snow skiing before.
8. I've .... taken 100 photos today.

2 Complete the conversations. Write questions or complete answers in the present perfect. Use <u>already</u>, <u>yet</u>, <u>ever</u>, or <u>before</u>.

1. **A:** .... ?
   B: Yes, they have. Jose and Ana went horseback riding just last month.

2. **A:** Have you already taken the bus tour?
   B: No. We ....

3. **A:** Has Ben ever tried matcha green tea?
   B: Yes. He ....

4. **A:** .... ?
   B: Yes. We've been to the Bahamas twice.

5. **A:** .... ?
   B: No, but they plan to go to the top of the Eiffel Tower on Saturday.

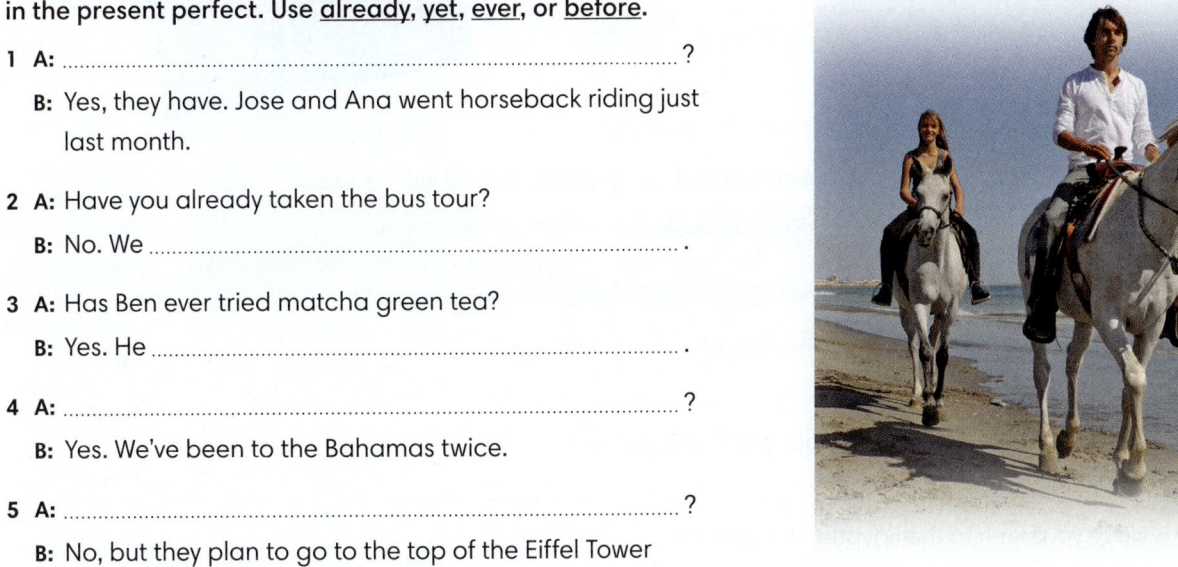

3 Look at Lisa and Patrick's to-do list for their vacation in Toronto. Lisa has checked what they have already done.

> ✓ – take a tour of the university
> ✓ – meet Michel for dinner on Spadina Avenue
>   – visit the Bata Shoe Museum
> ✓ – see a musical downtown
>   – take a boat trip around Toronto Harbor
> ✓ – go shopping at the Eaton Centre

Now finish Lisa's postcard to her friend. Write what she and Patrick have already done and what they haven't done yet. Use the present perfect.

Dear Jodi,   Sunday, August 10

Patrick and I are having a wonderful time in Toronto. We've done so many things already! _____

_____
_____
_____
_____
_____
_____

See you when we get back!
Love,
Lisa

4 Complete the conversation with sentences from the box. Not all will be used.

> Actually, it's my first time. I arrived last Wednesday.   Me? I'm from Egypt.
> Me? I'm from Wisconsin, in the US.   No, I haven't.   No, I haven't. I don't like museums.
> Thanks for the suggestion!   Yes, I have. I love museums.

A: I hope you don't mind my asking, but where are you from?

B: (1) ....

A: Welcome to Egypt! Have you been to Cairo before?

B: (2) ....

A: Have you been to the Egyptian Museum?

B: (3) ....

A: Me too. What about the Cairo Tower? Have you been there yet?

B: (4) ....

A: Well, it's awesome. You should definitely go.

B: (5) ....

LESSON 3

1 Read the blog. Which statement is true for all three posts? Circle the correct answer.

a They are all about trips taken to learn from an expert teacher.

b They are all about trips related to people's hobbies.

c They are all about trips to more than one city.

Travel with a Twist: A Blog for Unique Travel Experiences

Do you have an interesting travel tale to tell? Post it here for travel fans everywhere to enjoy!

Have you ridden the Chess Train? Posted 3d 7h
A couple of years ago, I rode on the Chess Train through five cities in three east European countries. It was amazing! Each passenger car had one long table with chairs for 20 people to play chess as we rolled along. My opponents were mostly German, Czech, or Austrian. We shook hands before each game, and win, lose, or draw, I always made a new friend. When the train stopped, my fellow chess players and I went on interesting walking tours together. The centuries-old stone buildings we saw were really impressive! I posted photos of them and the Chess Train online. It was really the trip of a lifetime.

Pottery meets tourism in Japan Posted 2d 2h
My hobbies are travel and pottery. Last summer, I enjoyed both of them on a pottery tour of Japan with my friend Alia. We visited several pottery workshops and pottery museums in different regions. I was surprised to see so many different styles! I like Bizen ware the most. It's simple but beautiful. We took a scenic train ride through mountains and rice paddies to Okayama prefecture, where Bizen ware is made. There, we met Mr. Kyo Isezaki, the greatest maker of Bizen ware in Japan, at his workshop. We bowed to each other, and then he explained some of the secrets of making great pottery. It was so exciting! This trip really improved my pottery skills!

Cooking the Italian way! Posted 1d 13h
I'm a real food lover. So, when I saw an ad for a seven-day cooking vacation in Umbria, Italy, I invited my wife to go! We stayed with other travelers in a lovely farmhouse in the scenic Italian countryside. There were beautiful Italian paintings on the walls and green hills all around. It was so relaxing! We went shopping with our teacher for ingredients at local farms, and everything was super fresh! I learned to make all sorts of Umbrian pasta dishes, soups, and pizzas. I fell in love with Umbrian pecorino cheese. My favorite used to be Taleggio, but now I like pecorino even more. It's a sheep's milk cheese that they've made the same way for 2,000 years. What a wonderful food tradition!

2 Reread the blog in Exercise 1. Then read the statements. Which trips do they describe? Circle all of the correct answers.

1 The blogger went on the tour with a friend or family member. (Chess Train / pottery tour / cooking tour)
2 The blogger enjoyed seeing different works of art. (Chess Train / pottery tour / cooking tour)
3 The blogger visited more than one country. (Chess Train / pottery tour / cooking tour)
4 The blogger went shopping. (Chess Train / pottery tour / cooking tour)
5 The blogger enjoyed viewing the countryside. (Chess Train / pottery tour / cooking tour)
6 The blogger met a famous person. (Chess Train / pottery tour / cooking tour)

3 Review the blog in Exercise 1 again. Match each word or phrase to its definition. Draw a line.

1 draw
2 opponent
3 prefecture
4 Taleggio
5 Bizen ware
6 paddy

a a person who tries to defeat you in a game
b a type of cheese
c a type of pottery
d a game that ends with no winner
e a field where people grow rice
f an area like a state within a country

LESSON 4

1 Look at the pictures. Complete each sentence with a participial adjective from the box.

| amazed | confused | depressed | disappointed | embarrassed | surprised | tired |
| amazing | confusing | depressing | disappointing | embarrassing | surprising | tiring |

1 The soccer game was .... Dustin was .... when his team lost.

2 Boni is very .... after her run. The run was ....

3 The view is .... Tisha is ....

4 Cheyanne was .... when she saw the gift. The gift was really ....

5 Bailey was .... when she saw that her wallet was empty. It was so .... !

6 The map is .... Kaitlyn is ....

16   UNIT 2

2 Read the sentences. How does the speaker feel about each situation? Write the correct letter.

.... 1 My friend Celeste loves to go zip lining. I've never done it because I'm way too scared.
.... 2 I received a beautiful bouquet of flowers today and it's not even my birthday. I have no idea who sent them.
.... 3 Gilbert likes playing sports, but he's not really in shape. He needs to rest frequently while playing.
.... 4 We were excited about getting bonuses this year, but the checks weren't very big. We were a bit let down.
.... 5 The view from the top floor of our office is spectacular. We can't get over how beautiful it is.
.... 6 Alice can't understand why Chase suddenly stopped answering her texts. He's acting very strange and she doesn't know what to do.

a He finds it tiring.
b She finds it terrifying.
c They were disappointed by it.
d We found it amazing.
e She was surprised by it.
f She's confused by it.

3 Complete the chart. Write about memorable things you've done and things you haven't done but want to do.

	Things I've done	Things I want to do
climb	climb Mt. Kilimanjaro	climb Mt. Everest
try		
go sightseeing in		
take a tour of		
go to the top of		
ride		
walk along		
take pictures of		

4 Look at your experiences in Exercise 3. Write about three things you've done using <u>already</u> or <u>before</u>. Describe each experience with a participial adjective.

> I've already climbed Mt. Kilimanjaro in Tanzania. It was thrilling!

1.
2.
3.

Now write about three things you haven't done but want to do. Use <u>yet</u>, <u>have never</u>, or <u>haven't ever</u>.

1.
2.
3.

UNIT 2

GRAMMAR EXPANDER

1 Complete each sentence. Circle the correct form of the verb.

1. Kevin is afraid of flying, so he (has taken / took) the train on his last vacation.
2. Amy (has been / went) to the Pocono mountains several times.
3. Our family (traveled / has traveled) to Ireland last summer.
4. We (ate / 've eaten) at this same table for many years.
5. I (stayed / had stayed) at home cleaning all day on Saturday.
6. I ('ve learned / learned) a lot about making my own bread dough.
7. She (has washed / washed) clothes all morning.
8. We (went / 've gone) sightseeing when we were in New York.

2 Correct the errors in the following sentences. In some cases, more than one answer is correct.

1. They've taken a tour of the Grand Canyon yet.

2. She has before been to New Zealand.

3. Already he has learned English and French.

4. Josephine hasn't yet had her lunch.

5. Has Rudy before been to Canada?

6. I haven't never tried escargot.

3 Rewrite each sentence using the words in parentheses. Make any necessary changes. There may be more than one correct answer.

1. (before) He's been to the Louvre in Paris.
2. (ever) Have you ridden a cable car?
3. (already) We have seen this musical four times.
4. (yet) I haven't shaken hands with someone famous.
5. (yet) She isn't ready to settle down.
6. (already) We can't go out. I made dinner.
7. (before) Have you gone ice fishing?
8. (ever) Have you changed careers?

DID YOU KNOW . . . ?
History of the Handshake
Shaking hands was a way of making sure that people were not carrying a weapon such as a knife or sword. When you shook hands, you were saying, "Look, I don't have a weapon. I trust you. Let's be friends."

WRITING HANDBOOK

1 Correct the run-on sentences. Use a period to separate the independent clauses or combine them with <u>and</u> or <u>but</u>.

1 Anthony studies often he gets good grades.
....

2 I've been to London before it was quite a trip.
....

3 We rode horses when we were younger, we don't ride them now.
....

4 Denise has never traveled outside of the U.S. before she has been to 40 states.
....

5 I have never been to the Shanghai Tower, I hear the view is amazing.
....

6 I recognize you, we met before, we were on the same sightseeing tour yesterday.
....

7 We've tried sushi before we think it is delicious.
....

8 She's from Spain, she has studied English, now she would like to learn Russian.
....

2 Write a letter to an old friend. Write about what you've been up to in the past year. Use the ideas as a guide. Check for run-on sentences. Use a period to separate the independent clauses or use <u>and</u> or <u>but</u> to combine them.

> Hi Janice! How have you been? I've been so busy but I wanted to write and catch up with you. In March, I started a new English class . . .

Ideas
You've . . .
  gotten engaged / married
  changed careers
  started a new job / class
  moved
  taken a vacation / business trip
  been busy

UNIT 2

UNIT 3 Talking about Movies

Warm-up

1 Match each movie genre with the correct description. Write the letter on the line.

1 .... feature scary or frightening situations that make us afraid
2 .... make us laugh and smile
3 .... give us information about real people and things
4 .... feature fast-paced, exciting, and dangerous situations
5 .... focus on character's problems and emotions
6 .... usually take place in the future
7 .... are drawn by hand or created on a computer
8 .... tell a story with singing and dancing

a action movies
b animated movies
c comedies
d documentaries
e dramas
f horror movies
g musicals
h science-fiction movies

2 Read each description. What kind of movie is it? Circle the correct answer.

1 People who enjoy singing and dancing usually like these.
   a dramas   b musicals   c documentaries

2 In the old days, artists drew thousands of pictures to make this kind of movie. Today, they often use computers.
   a horror movie   b action movie   c animated movie

3 Some people are fascinated by movies that feature robots, spacecrafts, or alien worlds.
   a science-fiction b comedy   c musical

4 If you like information about real people and things, you probably like these. They are great for learning.
   a musicals   b comedies   c documentaries

5 I don't go to movies like this, and I don't let my children watch them on TV. They're very frightening.
   a horror movies   b action movies   c dramas

6 Are you feeling sad? Do you need a good laugh? See one of these, and you might feel better!
   a action movie   b comedy   c horror movie

3 Write the correct statement for each meaning. Use sentences from the box.

| I could use a good laugh. | I'm beat. | It's a classic. | Our treat. | We insist. | What the heck. |

An expression you use when . . .
1 you describe an old movie that people still love today: ....
2 you're really tired: ....
3 you offer to pay the bill: ....
4 you want to emphasize your willingness to do something: ....
5 you'd like to see something funny: ....
6 you're not sure you want to do something but decide to do it anyway: ....

LESSON 1

1 Look at the pictures. Then complete the conversation.

Becky: Hi, Vicki. Sorry I'm late. Have you been waiting long?

Vicki: For about fifteen minutes. What happened?

Becky: Well, first **(1)** .... I ran to catch it but it pulled away before I got there. Then **(2)** .... because it was raining. So, I went back home to get my car. Of course, then **(3)** .... Finally, I made it here but **(4)** .... It took me about five minutes before I found a spot.

Vicki: Well, you're here now. Let's go see the movie!

2 Complete the sentences with phrases from the box.

| couldn't find a parking space | get a taxi | got stuck in traffic | missed the bus | overslept again |

1. I can't believe I .... There must be something wrong with my alarm clock.
2. Jackson had to park his car 10 blocks away. He .... near the office.
3. Abbey is going to be late. Her car is in the shop and she ....
4. It is so hard to .... when it's raining. They seem to just drive right by.
5. Because of the accident on the main highway, Carlito ....

3 Complete the posting from an online movie message board. Use <u>since</u> or <u>for</u>.

Movie Reviews > Disappointing Action Movies
Name: Veeck   Date: 7/10 8:12 a.m.   Post # 5

Comments: I've been an action movie fan _____ 20 years, _____ I was 11 years old. I
                                                    (1)   (2)
haven't seen a good one _____ a very long time. Last night I saw the movie *Underwater*, and it
                              (3)
was terrible. I watched it for about an hour, but then I had to turn it off. I kept falling asleep! It was

the worst action movie I've seen _____ 1997, when I saw *Batman and Robin*. In my opinion,
                                       (4)
there still haven't been any good action movies _____ *Avengers: Endgame* in 2019. What a
                                                      (5)
disappointment!

UNIT 3

4 Complete each sentence with the words in parentheses. Use the present perfect + <u>for</u> or <u>since</u>. Use contractions when possible.

1 *He's been a Bollywood star for* 20 years. (he / be / a Bollywood star)
2 .... I was a child. (I / not / ride / a bike)
3 .... five years. (she / work / at the bank)
4 .... a long time. (I / love / animated movies)
5 .... quite a while. (we / not / be / to a movie theater)
6 Sandra Bullock .... he was in his 20s. (be / my husband / favorite actress)
7 .... over a decade. (they / watch / movies / together)
8 .... it first came out. (he / want / to see / that documentary)
9 .... we can't go out tonight. (We / should / stream / that action movie)

5 Complete the conversation with phrases from the box. Not all the phrases will be used.

> 7:00 showing   a long time   about ten   are on me   at 7:30   let me get   my treat   pretty funny   Sorry I'm late

A: **(1)** .... I couldn't find parking. Have you been here long?
B: For **(2)** .... minutes, maybe. But no worries.
A: Have you checked the movie times?
B: Yes. Unfortunately, the **(3)** .... of *Soul* is sold out. But *The Croods: A New Age* is playing later, **(4)** .... I heard it's **(5)** ....
A: OK, sounds good. Let's do that. Hey, **(6)** .... the tickets.
B: That's really not necessary.
A: I insist! It's **(7)** ....

LESSON 2

1 Complete the sentences. Circle the correct words.

1 This is the (three times / third time / third movie) we've watched *Jason Bourne*.
2 Have you been to any good comedies (recently / always / still)?
3 We (so far / still / just) saw the movie *Soul*. It was so good.
4 I (still / just / recently) haven't seen *Wonder Woman 1984*. Have you?
5 How many Harry Potter movies have there been (so far / still / always)?
6 I've (still / recently / always) wanted to see *The Wizard of Oz* on stage.
7 That was one of the (best / better / good) movies I've seen in years.
8 *Braveheart* is one of the (amazing / most amazing / so amazing) movies ever made.

22   UNIT 3

2
Complete each sentence with the words in parentheses. Use the present perfect. Use contractions when possible.

1. *This is the first time I've ever visited Miami.* (ever / I / visit / Miami)
2. It's the saddest movie .... (ever / I / see)
3. You haven't missed much. The movie .... (just / start)
4. .... any movie reviews recently? (your sister / write)
5. .... to take a behind-the-scenes tour of a movie studio. (always / I / want)
6. This is the second time .... to see that new science-fiction movie, but the tickets keep selling out. (we / try)
7. She still .... the latest *Avengers* movie. (not / see)

3
Write the correct word to complete each sentence. Use contractions when possible.

1. **A:** This movie is boring. Is there something else you'd .... watch?
   B: No. Let's just turn off the TV.
2. **A:** I'd rather go to a movie than eat out tonight. How about you?
   B: Actually, ... rather not go out at all.
3. **A:** Would you rather see an action movie or a romance?
   B: .... one. I'd rather see a comedy.
4. **A:** Are we going to meet your brother downtown tonight?
   B: No, I'd rather .... I don't want to get stuck in traffic.
5. **A:** Which would you rather have? Pizza or pasta.
   B: Oh, I'd rather .... pizza, please. Extra pepperoni.

4
Complete the conversations. Write the words in parentheses in the correct order.

1. (Chris / see / rather / would)
   A: *Would Chris rather see* a comedy or an action movie?
   B: Definitely a comedy. He can't stand action movies.

2. (go / rather / you / where / would)
   A: .... , to the Theater Royale or Prime Time Cinema?
   B: I prefer the Theater Royale.

3. (she / would / watch / rather)
   A: .... something on TV tonight?
   B: Yes, I think she would. She seems tired.

4. (rather / with / ride / us)
   A: Would your friends .... than take a taxi?
   B: Yes, I'm sure they would.

5. (I / not / rather / would)
   A: Would you rather go to the 10:00 P.M. show?
   B: No, ...

UNIT 3

5 Write statements about your own preferences. Use the words in parentheses and <u>would rather</u>.

1 (stream a movie at home / go to a theater) *I would rather go to a theater than stream a movie at home*.

2 (eat rice / pasta) ....

3 (watch a comedy / a science fiction movie) ....

4 (go shopping / exercise at the gym) ....

5 (listen to rock music / classical music) ....

6 (take a trip to the mountains / the beach) ....

6 Complete the conversation with sentences from the box.

> Hi, Chrissy! How about a movie tonight?
> Is it an action movie?
> It's a science fiction thriller by Christopher Nolan.
> No offense, but I hate horror movies. I'd rather see something exciting like *Tenet*.
> That sounds great. I've been wanting to see a good sci fi movie.
> That works for me. What are you in the mood for—a horror movie?

A: (1) ....
B: (2) ....
A: (3) ....
B: (4) ....
A: (5) ....
B: (6) ....

LESSON 3

1 Match the words and their definitions. Draw a line.

1 thought-provoking   a something that makes you think
2 boring   b something you are going to remember
3 silly   c strange or unusual, in a negative way
4 romantic   d with a lot of fighting and killing
5 unforgettable   e not serious, almost stupid
6 hilarious   f not interesting
7 violent   g very, very funny
8 weird   h about love

2 Complete the paragraphs with adjectives in the box.

boring   funny   hilarious   romantic   silly   thought-provoking   unforgettable   violent   weird

Giovanni

My family enjoys comedies. They're usually so (1) .... , and the really good ones are (2) .... But sometimes there are really bad ones, like *Dirty Grandpa*. We were surprised because it was so stupid and gross. It didn't make us laugh at all. It was (3) .... and disgusting, and we left the movie theater after 30 minutes. We've never done that before, so I guess that makes this movie (4) .... for us! We'll always remember it because it was so bad!

Harper

I love action movies with a good plot and lots of fighting and killing. I think they're thrilling! Most of my girlfriends disagree with me. Yesterday, my friend Sue told me, "I prefer (5) .... movies showing people in love. I don't like action movies because they're too bloody and (6) .... But you're different. To tell you the truth, sometimes I think your movie tastes are a little (7) .... !"

Jackson

My wife, Veronica, is fascinated by documentaries, but I'm not. I usually find them slow and, to be honest, (8) .... Well, last night was different. We watched a program about life in the future, and we both loved it because it was so interesting. How will our lives be different in the next ten, twenty, and fifty years? I've never really thought about that. It was a very serious and (9) .... show.

3 Write a sentence about a movie that matches each adjective.

1 (funny) *Jumanji: The Next Level is very funny. Dwayne Johnson, Jack Black, and Kevin Hart are hilarious.*
2 (hilarious) ....
3 (unforgettable) ....
4 (thought-provoking) ....
5 (romantic) ....
6 (silly) ....
7 (violent) ....

DID YOU KNOW...?

MOVIE HISTORY

1890: movies invented. The first movies were about a minute long and had no sound.

1905: first movie theater: The Nickelodeon, in Pittsburgh, Pennsylvania, US. Still no sound—a piano player would play live music during the movie.

1906: first full-length movie: *The Story of the Kelly Gang*. Early movies were called "motion pictures," "moving pictures," or "photoplays."

1927: first movie with sound: *The Jazz Singer*. At first, these new types of movies were called "talking pictures" or "talkies."

LESSON 4

1 Read the article. What is it mainly about? Circle the correct answer.

a why moviemakers should try to make classic movies

b why audiences should prefer some movies over others

c why some movies become less popular while others remain popular

Movies and the Test of Time

Just because a movie wins awards today doesn't mean it will remain a favorite. *Argo* (2012) and *Crash* (2006) each won the Oscar for best picture, but they have far fewer fans today. On the other hand, movies like *Titanic* (1997) and *Star Wars* (1977) continue to fascinate new generations of moviegoers. Let's look at a few reasons why some movies become outdated while others remain timeless classics.

Floppy disks, cassette tapes, and other old technologies make a movie look old-fashioned. Even with the star power of Keanu Reeves, *Johnny Mnemonic* (1995) is difficult to watch now due to all the out-of-date technology. The same is true for *The Net* (1995) with Sandra Bullock. However, nearly three decades before, *2001: A Space Odyssey* (1968) did a better job of showing us the future, and its depiction of artificial intelligence still amazes modern audiences.

Changing social attitudes can also affect the popularity of certain movies. *Gone with the Wind*, *Breakfast at Tiffany's*, and *Raiders of the Lost Ark*, long considered among the greatest movies ever made, are viewed less often these days. One reason is the racial stereotypes that they contain. Decades ago, viewers thought little of the falseness of these depictions, whereas today they are considered offensive.

A *period piece* is a movie that takes place during a particular period in history. Since such movies depict a time in the past that never changes, the clothing, hairstyles, and background details never go out of style. But to become a classic, it also helps if they avoid stereotypes and include themes that are still meaningful for us today. *Schindler's List*, *Raise the Red Lantern*, and *Lincoln* are just three examples of timeless period pieces.

Animation and superhero movies set in fantasy worlds created by human imagination also avoid the problems mentioned above. This helps explain why, in a recent poll, movie fans aged 13–37 placed *The Avengers*, *Harry Potter*, *Star Wars*, *The Lord of the Rings*, and *Jurassic Park* among their favorites of all time. Three love stories also made their top 10: *Titanic*, *The Notebook*, and *Pride and Prejudice*. After all, love never goes out of style.

2 Read the article in Exercise 1 again. Complete the sentences. Circle the correct words.

1 The movie *Crash* is (more popular than / less popular than / as popular as) it was in 2006.

2 According to the author, the problem with *Johnny Mnemonic* is (too little star power / old technology / an out-of-date story).

3 An older movie with a vision of technology that still pleases audiences today is (*The Net* / *Argo* / *2001: A Space Odyssey*).

4 *Gone with the Wind* is becoming less popular because (it contains racial stereotypes / it was made in 1940 / it has movie stars that nobody remembers).

5 *Schindler's List* will never look out-of-date because it (won the Oscar for best picture / has little technology in it / is a period piece).

6 (Action movies / Dramas / Fantasy movies) are least likely to have problems discussed in the article.

7 *Star Wars*, *Titanic*, and (*Breakfast at Tiffany's* / *Raiders of the Lost Ark* / *Jurassic Park*) are still popular with young audiences.

3 Complete the sentences with words from the article in Exercise 1.

1 A .... is a common idea of what a type of person is like, which is often not correct.
2 Although Marilyn Monroe died long ago, she continues to .... moviegoers.
3 A .... movie is one that will be enjoyed by future generations as much as it is today.
4 If you have a good ...., you can easily form pictures or ideas in your mind.
5 Something that is .... is very impolite and is likely to upset people.

GRAMMAR EXPANDER

1 Put the words in the correct order to form information questions in the present perfect.

1 How / *The Queen's Gambit* / times / watched / have / many / you
....?

2 has / the / Who / special effects / best / created
....?

3 documentary / directed / she / Why / a / ever / hasn't
....?

4 Which / enjoyed / movie / action / you / have / most / the
....?

5 free / tickets / How many / received / he / for / times / has / the theater
....?

6 coming / Where / here / before / Betty / has / worked
....?

7 her / have / watched / Which / you / of / musicals
....?

8 Who / the most / reviewed / have / critics / the
....?

2 Write sentences and questions about preferences. Use the words in parentheses.

1 (Tim / would rather / drive / take the train)
....?

2 (Sasha / not / would rather / watch / a horror movie)
....?

3 (Who / stream / would like / a funny movie / tonight)
....?

4 (I'd rather / tomorrow / go / to the movie theater)
....?

5 (They / see / would like / the latest science-fiction movie)
....?

6 (My husband / meet / would rather / at the restaurant)
....?

3 Look at the answers. Write questions with <u>like</u>, <u>prefer</u>, or <u>would rather</u>. There is more than one correct answer.

1 **A:** ....?
B: It doesn't matter to me. You choose.

2 **A:** ....?
B: I'd rather go to the Premier Theater.

3 **A:** ....?
B: I'd prefer an action movie tonight.

4 **A:** ....?
B: No. I don't like scary movies.

5 **A:** ....?
B: We'd rather stay in and stream a movie.

WRITING HANDBOOK

1 Read the paragraph. Write a topic sentence.

Topic sentence: ....

People don't usually imitate the behavior they see in movies. They know it is make-believe. Would you try jumping from the roof of one tall building to another just because you saw it in an action movie? We live in a violent world. Just open any newspaper—or history book. What happens in real life is often more violent than what happens in movies, and violence is not new. Violent entertainment has been around for a very long time. Think about the gladiators in ancient Rome.

2 Write two paragraphs about a talented actor. In the first paragraph, write about the actor's best movies, what they are about, and how you feel about them. In the second paragraph, describe the actor's performances and why you think this actor is one of the best. Include a topic sentence for each paragraph.

> I think Saoirse Ronan is a very talented actor. She has been in a lot of excellent movies. Her best one is Brooklyn. It is about...

Ideas
makes us laugh
is multi-talented
wows audiences
plays a variety of roles

28 UNIT 3

UNIT 4 Away from Home

Warm-up

1 Look at the picture. Write the hotel amenities.

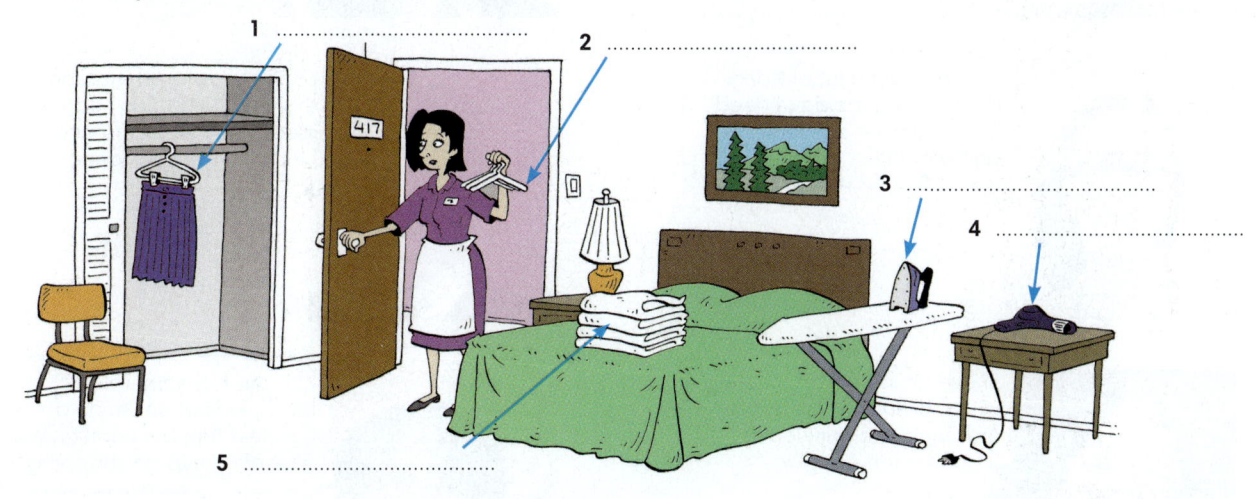

1 ....
2 ....
3 ....
4 ....
5 ....

2 Look at the pictures. Then complete the conversations.

A: Guest services. May I help you?
B: Yes, please. Could you bring up some **(1)** ....? I need clean ones.
A: Certainly.
B: And I could use a **(2)** ...., too. My hair is wet, and I don't see one in the bathroom.
A: Sure. We'll bring those up right away. Anything else?
B: Oh, yes. I have a lot of clothes. Could someone please bring me extra **(3)** ....?
A: Yes, of course.
B: I think that's all. Thanks!

A: Front Desk. May I help you?
B: Yes, I'd like to go for a swim. Is the **(4)** .... still open?
A: No, I'm sorry, it closed at 9:00.
B: Oh. Well, maybe a workout. How about the **(5)** ....?
A: No, it also just closed.
B: Oh, no. Well, I guess I'll have to do some work then. Is the **(6)** .... still open?
A: No, I'm sorry. It closed at 6:30. But you do have high-speed Internet access in your room.
B: Oh, OK. Thanks.

3 Read what each hotel guest says. Which facilities and amenities are important to them? Write the hotel facility or amenity on the line.

I like to swim before I have breakfast. It's a great way to start the day!

1 ....

I want a safe place to put my money and other valuables when I'm out of the hotel.

2 ....

I need to get a lot of work done during the day. I need a fast Internet connection and a printer.

3 ....

I don't know anything about this city. I'm hoping I can get ideas for sightseeing and help with transportation.

4 ....

I have an important meeting with a client. My suit has to look nice, not wrinkled.

5 ....

I always buy something for my kids when I'm on a business trip, but I don't have a lot of time to go shopping.

6 ....

4 What hotel service or amenity is important to you when you travel? Explain why.

_____
_____
_____
_____
_____
_____

DID YOU KNOW . . . ?
Top 5 Most Important Hotel Amenities
Surveys show that travelers prefer free Internet connections over any other hotel amenity.
1. free Wi-Fi
2. free breakfast
3. indoor swimming pool
4. hotel restaurant
5. queen or king-size beds

5 Match the phrases on the left to their meanings on the right. Draw a line.

1 I'm with you.   a It's expensive.
2 It costs an arm and a leg. b There are a lot of negative points.
3 Look at the fine print.   c I agree.
4 It's got a lot of downsides. d Read it carefully.

30 UNIT 4

LESSON 1

1 Match the words on the left to their definitions on the right. Write the letter.

.... 1 a greeting
.... 2 an answering machine
.... 3 an answering service
.... 4 a voicemail

a a message that a caller records on someone else's phone or answering machine
b a service that takes calls and messages for other people
c a device that records messages from callers
d a message that automatically plays when a person can't answer the phone

2 Complete the sentences with words from the box.

| greeting machine operator service voicemail |

1 My new answering .... is not very good. They don't deliver my messages on time and they get information wrong.
2 Did you get the message that Sarah left on your answering .... ?
3 If you'd like to make an appointment, call this number and speak to the ....
4 Alessandro got a new cellphone. He needs to record a .... for people who call when he can't answer.
5 I left a .... on your phone. Did you get my message?

3 The fortune-teller is predicting the future. Read her predictions. Then rewrite the sentences using **will**.

1 Next week, you are going to win some money.
2 Then, you're taking a trip to Panama.
3 While in Panama, you run into an old friend.
4 Your friend is going to offer you an exciting job.
5 Next month, you are moving to Panama.

1 ....
2 ....
3 ....
4 ....
5 ....

4 Rewrite the future statements and questions using **will**.

1 I'm going to use the fitness center later today. ....
2 Where is your wife staying while in Detroit? ....
3 Who is Angelica going to meet with on Monday? ....
4 What time does the gift shop open? ....

UNIT 4   31

5 Put the conversation in order. Write the number on the line.

_1_ Can I speak with Connor Williams, please? He's staying in room 455.
..... Yes, that's it. Thank you very much.
..... That's right.
..... One moment, please . . . I'm sorry. There's no answer. Can I take a message?
..... Dakota at 228-555-3150?
..... Could you tell him Dakota called? Please ask him to call me back at 228-555-3150.
..... Is that all?

6 Read the phone conversation. Then complete the message slip.

A: Hello. I'd like to speak with Ms. Eileen Hernandez, please.

B: One moment, please. I'll ring Ms. Hernandez's room . . . I'm sorry, but there's no answer. Would you like to call back later?

A: No, I'd like to leave a message. Please tell her that Hannah Denson called. I'll be at 275-555-8123 until 5:00 today if she can return my call.

B: OK, Ms. Hannah Benson . . .

A: No, it's Denson. That's "D" as in "door," – E-N-S-O-N.

B: OK, Ms. Denson. I'll make sure she gets the message.

A: Thank you.

TO: _Eileen Hernandez_
DATE: _11/7_ TIME: _4:00_   A.M. ☐   P.M. ☒
WHILE YOU WERE OUT
☐ Mr. ☐ Ms. ☐ Mrs. _____
Phone _____
 Area code Number Extension
☐ telephoned ☐ please call
☐ returned your call ☐ will call back
Message: _____

LESSON 2

1 Look at the pictures. Write the kind of hotel room or bed.

1 a ....

2 a ....
room

3 a ....
room

4 a .... bed

5 a .... bed

6 a .... bed

7 a .... bed

2 Complete the email message. Circle the correct kind of room or bed.

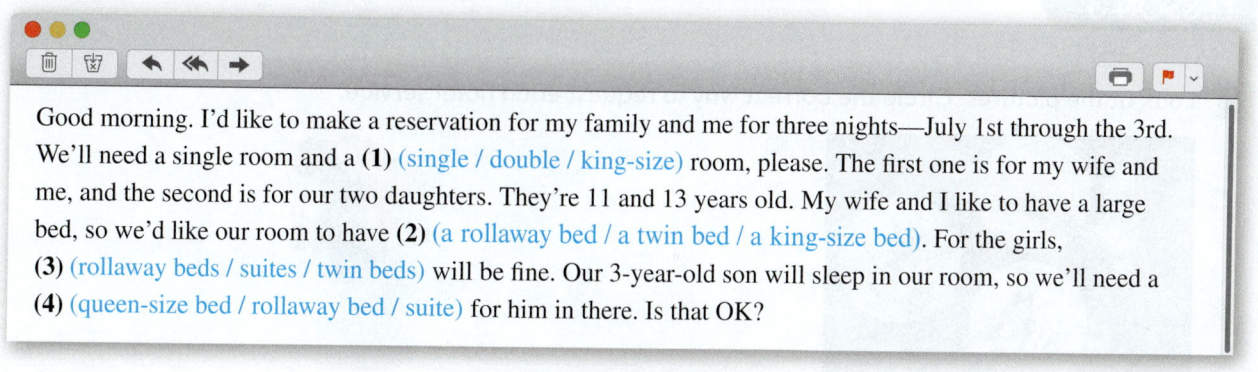

> Good morning. I'd like to make a reservation for my family and me for three nights—July 1st through the 3rd. We'll need a single room and a **(1)** (single / double / king-size) room, please. The first one is for my wife and me, and the second is for our two daughters. They're 11 and 13 years old. My wife and I like to have a large bed, so we'd like our room to have **(2)** (a rollaway bed / a twin bed / a king-size bed). For the girls, **(3)** (rollaway beds / suites / twin beds) will be fine. Our 3-year-old son will sleep in our room, so we'll need a **(4)** (queen-size bed / rollaway bed / suite) for him in there. Is that OK?

3 Circle the correct words to complete each sentence.
1. If we hurry, we (can catch / will have caught) the shuttle to baggage claim.
2. He won't stay at a hotel if they (won't / don't) have a business center.
3. If they have our room ready, we (are / 'll be) able to check in early.
4. If you request it, the hotel (will provide / provides) a wake-up service in the morning.
5. Who do we call if we (will have / have) questions about local transportation?
6. If a hotel (has / will have) a fitness center, (will it be / is it) usually open at all hours?
7. If the light on your hotel room phone (will flash / flashes), it means you have a message.

4 Complete each real conditional sentence with the words in parentheses. Use the correct form of the verb. Use contractions when possible.
1. *If you take my advice*, you'll stay at a hotel in the city center. (if / you / take / my advice)
2. .... if they don't have a double room available? (what / we / do)
3. If you need more towels, ... (you / have to / call / the front desk)
4. .... , I won't be able to sleep. (if / the pillows / be / too hard)
5. .... , you should call the concierge now. (if / you / need / a taxi / tomorrow)
6. If you stay at the Pacifica Hotel, ... (you / have / a wonderful experience)

5 Complete the conversation with words from the box. Not all words will be used.

| by the way | checking in | checking out | credit card | double room | name |

A: Hello! I'm **(1)** .... The name's Ezzell.
B: Do you have a reservation?
A: Yes. For a **(2)** .... with a king-size bed.
B: Oh, yes. Here it is. May I have your **(3)** .... ?
A: Here you go. Oh, **(4)** .... , I'm going to need a wake-up call at 7 tomorrow.
B: No problem.

UNIT 4

LESSON 3

1 Look at the pictures. Circle the correct way to request each hotel service.

1
a Could we get some extra glasses, please?
b I'd like to order room service, please.
c Could someone take away the dishes, please?

2
a Could someone please pick up the laundry?
b Could someone please take away the dishes?
c I'd like a wake-up call, please.

3
a Could someone please pick up the laundry?
b I'd like a wake-up call, please.
c Could someone please take away the dishes?

4
a Could we get some extra towels, please?
b I'd like to order room service, please.
c Could we get some extra pillows, please?

5
a I'd like a wake-up call, please.
b Could someone please make up the room?
c Could someone pick up the laundry, please?

6
a I'd like to order room service, please.
b Could someone please make up the room?
c Could we get some extra cups, please?

2 Match each situation to the correct request for hotel service. Write the letter. One answer isn't used.

.... 1 You have a very early flight out in the morning. You don't want to oversleep.

.... 2 There are three of you in the room, but only two sets of towels in the bathroom.

.... 3 You need your blouse and pants cleaned and ironed for a meeting tomorrow.

a Could we get some extra towels, please?
b Could someone please pick up the laundry?
c I'd like to order room service, please.
d I'd like a wake-up call, please.

LESSON 4

1 Read the travel guide. What information does it give about the hotels? Check all the correct answers.

☐ a cost ☐ b location ☐ c amenities ☐ d hotel services ☐ e hotel address

Sleeping in DUBLIN

HOME ROOMS GALLERY EXTENDED STAYS

The Morgan Hotel — $$$
Style, Nightlife
If you're crazy about style, the Morgan Hotel is your place. With very modern décor and designer furniture, this chic hotel is a favorite of people who work in fashion and music. The Morgan is located in the trendy Temple Bar district—an area popular with young people and *the* center of nightlife in Dublin. Note: Can be noisy at night.
restaurant, room service, laundry service, business center, Internet service, fitness room

The Aberdeen Lodge — $$
Atmosphere, Service
A short train ride from the Dublin city center, in a neighborhood of beautiful old homes and gardens, the Aberdeen Lodge is the perfect place for a quiet and relaxing stay. The friendly staff welcomes guests with tea and cookies and is very helpful with tourist advice. Suites feature working fireplaces. Don't miss breakfast in the lovely dining room overlooking the garden. Note: There is no elevator.
restaurant, room service, laundry service

The Camden Court — $$
Convenience, Location
The Camden Court is a large hotel that offers business travelers a good night's sleep and lots of amenities at an affordable price. Rooms are small but clean and comfortable. A short walk from Saint Stephen's Green, the location is perfect—close to tourist attractions, restaurants, and shopping. The Camden Court is a good choice for business or pleasure.
pool, sauna, fitness room, room service, business center, free Internet service, beauty salon, restaurant, free parking

Trinity College — $
Price, Location
Experience student life—without the exams!—at this beautiful, historic university located in the center of Dublin. From June to September, visitors can reserve single and double rooms while students are away for the summer holiday. Rooms are large and clean, but don't expect many amenities or services. Not all rooms have their own bathrooms.
cafeteria-style restaurant, free breakfast

$$$ Very expensive / $$ Moderately priced / $ Budget

2 Write an advantage and a disadvantage of each hotel, according the travel guide in Exercise 1.

Hotel	Advantage	Disadvantage
The Morgan Hotel		
The Aberdeen Lodge		
The Camden Court		
Trinity College		

3 Read about the people's needs and preferences. Use the travel guide in Exercise 1 to decide the best hotel for each person. Write statements with <u>If</u> and <u>will</u> / <u>won't</u>.

1 "I want to meet other people my age and walk to the clubs at night."

....

2 "I'm traveling this summer. Location is important to me, but I'm on a budget."

....

3 "We're looking forward to sipping tea in front of a warm fireplace."

....

4 "I'm attending a conference in Dublin. I'll need to wake up early, so I'd like someplace quiet."

....

UNIT 4   35

GRAMMAR EXPANDER

1 Look at the pictures. What do you think the man is going to do? Write sentences with a form of <u>be going to</u> or <u>not be going to</u>.

1 ....
2 ....
3 ....
4 ....
5 ....

2 Complete the conversation. Use the correct form of <u>be going to</u> if there is a plan for the future or <u>will</u> if there is not a plan. Use contractions if possible.

A: Have you decided where you are going on your vacation?
B: Yes, we have. We **(1)** .... (go) to Spain!
A: Wow! When **(2)** .... ? (leave)
B: We **(3)** .... (fly) out on the 15th.
A: That's fantastic. Where **(4)** .... ? (stay)
B: I don't know yet. I guess we **(5)** .... (find) something when we get there.

3 Complete the conversations. Use the words in parentheses and your own ideas.

1 **A:** I'm really looking forward to dinner. Where should we eat?
  B: .... (should)
2 **A:** When do they have to check out of their room?
  B: .... (have to)
3 **A:** Can we see a baseball game today?
  B: .... (can not)
4 **A:** I'm having a party this Saturday. I hope you can come.
  B: Sorry. .... (not be able to)
5 **A:** I'm going to be moving into a new apartment next week.
  B: That's great! .... (should be able to / help)
6 **A:** How are we getting to the airport tomorrow?
  B: .... (have to / call)

36 UNIT 4

4 Write present real conditional sentences. Use the verbs in parentheses.

1 Whenever the weather .... (be) bad, she .... (work) from home.
2 My father .... (stay) in nice hotels whenever he .... (travel).
3 My daughter .... (take) her lunch to school if she .... (not like) what they're serving.
4 My family .... (be) angry, if I .... (forget) to stop by the grocery store.
5 If we .... (like) this bed and breakfast, we .... (stay) here again.

WRITING HANDBOOK

1 Read each sentence. Write <u>CS</u> if it is a complete sentence. Write <u>F</u> if it is a fragment.

.... 1 Because it has a pool and a sauna.
.... 2 Since the hotel offers free breakfast, I save money on food.
.... 3 We don't know where to go for dinner.
.... 4 A budget hotel with a cafeteria-style restaurant.
.... 5 Even if you don't like shopping, you should check this shop out.
.... 6 Quiet, relaxing, and charming location.
.... 7 If you need extra hangers, call the front desk.
.... 8 Since it's close to tourist attractions.

2 What types of accommodations do you prefer when you travel? What facilities and amenities are important to you? Explain your opinion. Include at least three sentences that contain <u>because</u> or <u>since</u>. Check that there are no sentence fragments.

I prefer to stay at a bed and breakfast when I go on vacation. Because a delicious breakfast is included in the price, I always start the day with a happy feeling . . .

Ideas
hotel
youth hostel
bed and breakfast
campground
short-term vacation rental

UNIT 4 37

UNIT 5 Looking Good

Warm-up

1 Complete the word webs. Write personal care products on the lines.

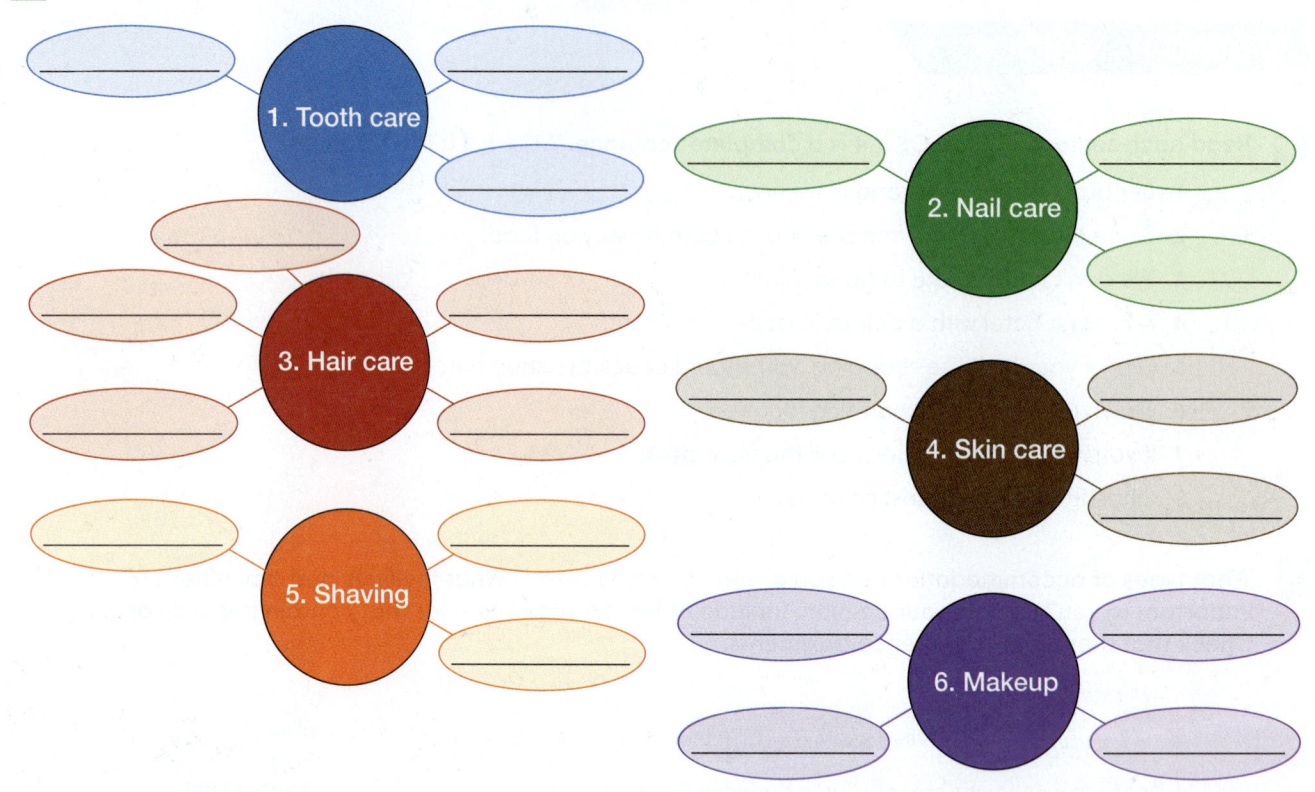

1. Tooth care
2. Nail care
3. Hair care
4. Skin care
5. Shaving
6. Makeup

2 Complete each sentence with the correct personal care product.

1. I need to cut my toenails. Do you know where the .... are?
2. I just finished washing my hair. Looks like we need more ....
3. It's so cold and windy today; my skin feels dry. I hope this .... will help.
4. My husband was shaving with a new .... this morning, and he cut his chin.
5. I heard it was going to be sunny today. If you'll be working outside, don't forget to put on some ....
6. When I get out of the shower, instead of using a brush, I typically run a .... through my hair.

DID YOU KNOW . . . ?

The average person has 125,000 strands of hair on his or her head and loses around 100 strands a day.

Hair is one of the fastest growing tissues in the body. It takes about 3 years to grow to the shoulders and 7 years to grow to the waist!

Hair color statistics
black: **84%**
brown: **11%**
blonde: **3%**
red: **2%**

3 Match the language on the left to the explanations on the right. Draw a line.

1 I don't care.
2 Go for it!
3 I'm ready to take the plunge.
4 While we're at it, lets . . .

a You're enthusiastically supporting someone's decision.
b You want to continue discussing a topic from a slightly different perspective.
c Announcing that you've made a decision to act.
d You don't mind if something happens.

LESSON 1

1 Complete the sentences. Circle some or any.

1 Are you out of hair gel? I have (some / any).
2 There's a sale on nail polish if you need (some / any).
3 Do you have (some / any) sunscreen I can use?
4 Please pick up deodorant while you're out. We don't have (some / any).
5 I just bought (some / any) shampoo yesterday.
6 Do you need (some / any) soap?

2 Complete the conversations. Write some or any + the words in parentheses.

1 A: I have ......*some lotion*...... if you need it. (lotion)
   B: Thanks, but I brought my own.
2 A: There's shaving cream in the bathroom if you need it.
   B: Actually, I looked, and there wasn't .... (in there)
3 A: Did you bring .... with you? (makeup)
   B: Oh, no. I forgot it on the bathroom counter.
4 A: Did you buy .... today? (razors)
   B: Yes, I put them in the cupboard under the sink.
5 A: Please get .... when you go to the store. (dental floss)
   B: OK. I added that to my list.
6 A: Would you mind if I borrowed your lipstick?
   B: No problem. I have .... (in my purse)

3 Complete the sentences with words from the box. Some words are used more than once.

| a lot | any | lots of | many | much | some |

1 I need .... hairspray. Do you have any?
2 She has .... of makeup. She needs more storage space.
3 This store doesn't have very .... brands of sunscreen.
4 They don't have .... lotion either.
5 Do you need .... aftershave?
6 You can have this nail polish. I don't wear ....
7 He uses .... skin care products. That's why he looks so good.
8 I picked up .... nail clippers today.

UNIT 5 39

4 Circle all the correct ways to complete each sentence.

1 I don't wear .... lipstick.
   a much
   b any
   c many

2 Did you buy .... shampoo?
   a many
   b any
   c some

3 Cody doesn't use .... personal care products.
   a a lot of
   b many
   c lots of

4 Eileen is wearing .... eye shadow.
   a a lot of
   b any
   c some

5 Do you need .... shaving cream?
   a many
   b some
   c any

6 That store doesn't have .... options for razors?
   a many
   b a lot of
   c much

5 Complete the sentences. Circle the correct words.

1 This store doesn't carry (**much** / many) personal care products.
2 I can't find (some / **any**) dental floss, but here are (**some** / any) toothbrushes.
3 Do you have (much / **a lot of**) combs and brushes?
4 I don't have (**much** / many) face powder left.
5 Clark needs (**some** / any) hair gel.
6 Grace doesn't use (some / **much**) shampoo.
7 Do you have (any / **many**) nail clippers?
8 I have (**some** / any) extra nail files if you need one.

6 Complete the conversation. Use phrases from the box. Not all of the phrases will be used.

| appreciate it | deodorant | for sunscreen | get some | hair care | makeup |
| mascara | right back | right over there | was some | wasn't any | |

A: Excuse me. I'm looking for some **(1)** ....

B: Mascara? That should be in aisle 3, in the **(2)** .... section.

A: I looked and there **(3)** ....

B: Oh, I'm sorry. Let me **(4)** .... from the back. Anything else?

A: Actually, yes. I need **(5)** ...., too.

B: No problem. There's some **(6)** ....

A: Thanks.

B: And I'll be **(7)** .... with some mascara.

A: Thanks. I **(8)** ....

UNIT 5

LESSON 2

1 Look at the pictures. Write the correct kind of personal care.

1 ....
2 .... 
3 .... 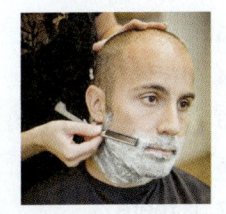
4 .... 
5 .... 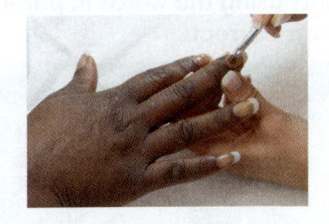
6 .... 

2 Complete the sentences. Circle the correct answer.

1 I like to keep my hair short, but it grows out so fast, so I schedule a (shave / haircut / massage / manicure) every five weeks.
2 Marjorie works at her desk all day. She doesn't always remember to get up and stretch, so her back aches. Marjorie would benefit from a (pedicure / manicure / massage / facial).
3 My husband has trimmed his beard for years, but he's thinking about cutting it off. He's looking for a salon that gives a good (shave / haircut / manicure / facial).
4 If we're wearing open-toed sandals for the party, I need to get a (massage / manicure / shave / pedicure).
5 Wow, Sharon! Your fingernails look great. Did you just get a (facial / pedicure / manicure / haircut)?
6 My skin is looking dry. I'm going to the spa for a (manicure / facial / pedicure / massage).

3 Look at the pictures. How often do you get these salon services? Write sentences using <u>never</u>, <u>often</u>, or <u>sometimes</u>.

1 ....
2 ....
3 ....
4 ....
5 ....

UNIT 5   41

4 Complete each statement or question with <u>someone</u>, <u>no one</u>, or <u>anyone</u>. There may be more than one correct answer.

1 Excuse me. .... is at the front desk. Can you help me?
2 I'm sorry. There isn't .... available to help you right now.
3 Can .... give me a manicure?
4 There's .... ahead of you. Do you mind waiting?
5 .... told me this was the best place to get a massage.
6 .... I know has been to this salon before.
7 Is there .... available to give me a shave?

5 Look at the picture. Write statements using the words in parentheses and <u>someone</u>, <u>no one</u>, or <u>anyone</u>. In some cases, more than one answer is correct.

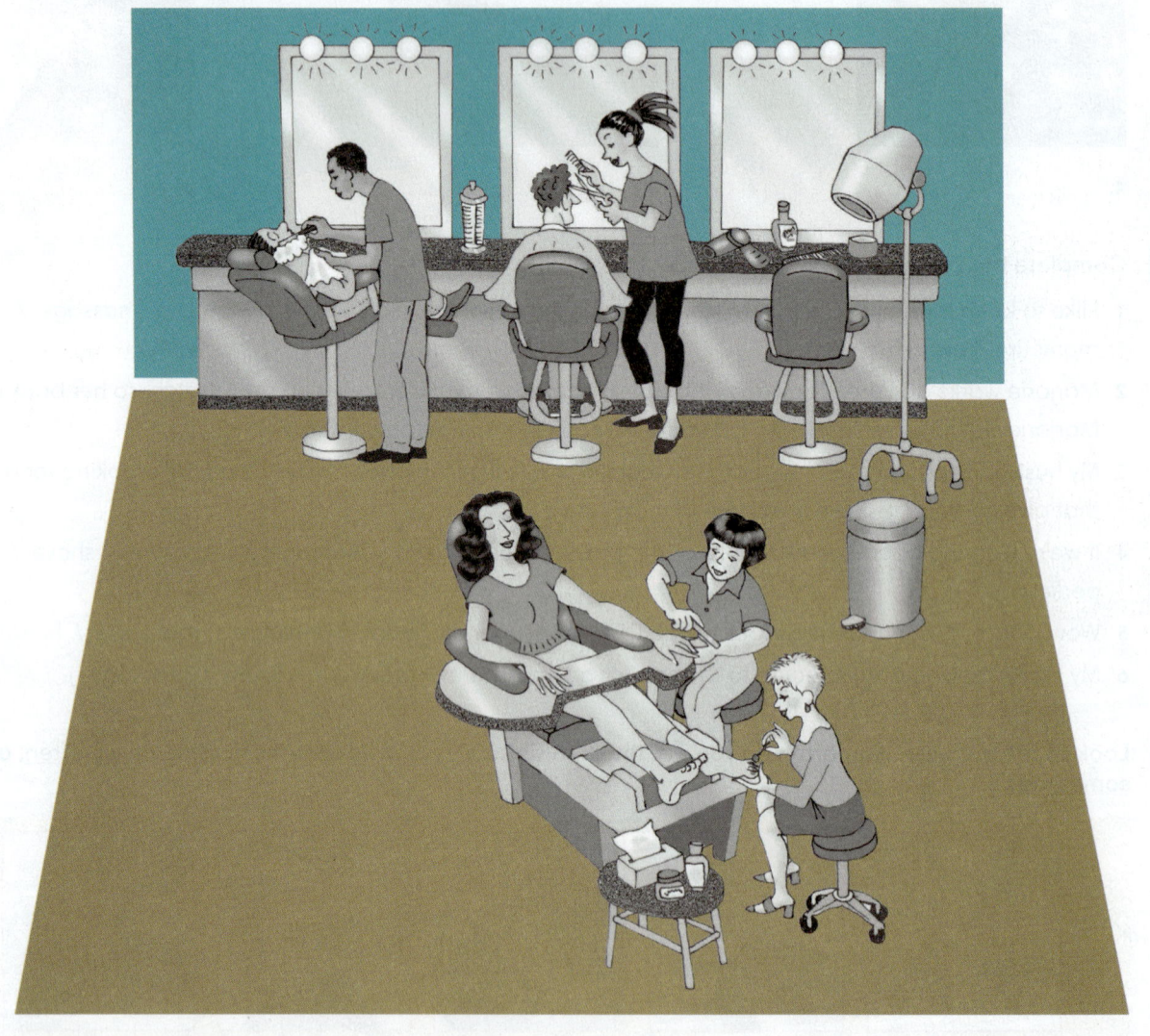

1 (get / manicure / pedicure) ....
2 (give / massage) ....
3 (use / razor) ....
4 (get / haircut) ....
5 (use / shampoo) ....
6 (use / comb) ....

6 Put the conversation in order. Write the number on the line.

__1__ **A:** Hello. Jenna's Salon.

_____ **B:** Actually, that won't work. I have a business lunch at 1:00. Is someone available after 4:00?

_____ **A:** Let me check, . . . Lisa has an opening at 12:30.

_____ **B:** Hi. This is Cindy Baker. I'd like to make an appointment for a massage.

_____ **A:** Yes. Edith can see you at 5:00. Would that work?

_____ **B:** Today, if possible. My back is very sore.

_____ **A:** When would you like to come in, Ms. Baker?

_____ **B:** Yes, that's perfect. Thank you.

LESSON 3

1 Look at the pictures. Write the correct cosmetic procedure.

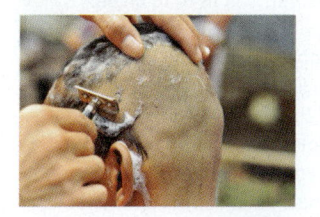

1 .... my ....

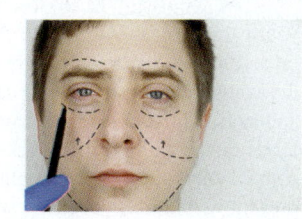

2 .... surgery

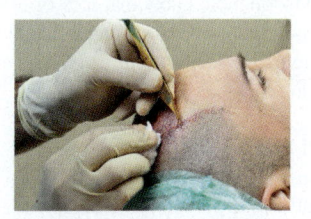

3 have a ....

4 .... my ....

5 .... a ....

6 .... my ....

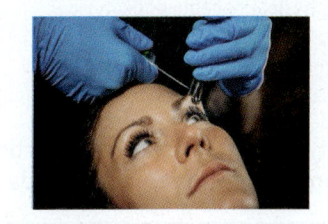

7 .... my ....

2 Circle the correct cosmetic procedures to complete the paragraph.

Angelica and her husband, Robert, recently had some cosmetic procedures done. Last week, she visited a local studio to get them to **(1)** (pierce her lip / pierce her eyebrow / pierce her ears). She is excited about wearing the new earrings she bought on their last vacation! Next week, she's going back to get another piercing—this time she wants to **(2)** (dye her hair / pierce her eyebrow / get a tattoo). Her husband is going bald. At first, he and Angelica talked about replacing the hair on his head, so he planned to **(3)** (dye his hair / have a hair transplant / shave his head). But some of Robert's friends told him that he would look better without any hair at all! So, he **(4)** (shaved his head / had a hair transplant / had cosmetic surgery) instead. He looks great! He also **(5)** (pierced his ears / got a tattoo / had cosmetic surgery) of an eagle on his arm. Both Angelica and Robert are happy with their faces overall, so they have no plans to **(6)** (have cosmetic surgery / get a tattoo / have a hair transplant). But Angelica is looking to do something a little different. She might **(7)** (shave her head / dye her hair / get a tattoo) a deep blue!

UNIT 5   43

LESSON 4

1 Read the article. What kind of information does it give? Circle the correct answer.

a ways to improve personal appearance
b low-cost cosmetic surgery
c tips to sleep better at night

Look Great — Without Cosmetic Surgery

Want to lose weight? Look younger? More and more people are turning to cosmetic surgery. While liposuction or a face-lift might sound like an easy way to get the results you want, it's important to remember that cosmetic surgery is, in fact, surgery. And surgery is not easy. It's expensive, painful, and potentially dangerous. So, before you go under the knife, give these safe, low-cost ways to improve your appearance, a try.

1. Get enough sleep. It's called "beauty sleep" for a reason. Nighttime is when your skin and hair cells renew and repair themselves. Also, more blood flows to your skin when you're sleeping, making it brighter. Most people know that lack of sleep can cause dark circles under your eyes. But many don't realize that not getting eight hours of sleep a night can also lead to wrinkles and weight gain.

2. Drink a lot of water. Get into the habit of drinking more water. Well-hydrated skin is less likely to develop blemishes or wrinkles. For clearer, smoother skin, try to drink at least eight glasses of water a day. The more water you drink, the better your skin will look. Also, drinking water throughout the day will curb your appetite—making it easier to eat less and lose weight.

3. Exercise regularly. The physical benefits of exercise include reduced body fat and more toned muscles. While 60 minutes of daily vigorous exercise is ideal, begin with a reasonable goal—maybe 30 minutes three times a week. Choose something you enjoy, and enroll in a class, join a team, or make plans to work out regularly with a group of friends.

4. Eat a healthy diet. To lose weight, you need to change your eating habits. You should choose foods that are low in fat and low in calories. You probably knew that already, but did you know that some foods can also improve the appearance of your skin and hair? For beautiful skin, eat foods rich in antioxidants. Dark-colored fruits and vegetables contain antioxidants, which help repair sun damage and prevent wrinkles. Blueberries, spinach, and carrots have a lot of antioxidants. For shiny, healthy hair, eat foods high in lean protein like fish, beans, and nuts. These foods may also help prevent hair loss. What's good for your health is also good for your looks. So, get a good night's sleep and some exercise. Drink lots of water and eat fresh, natural foods—mostly fruits and veggies. It costs almost nothing and doesn't hurt, so what have you got to lose? Except maybe a few pounds!

2 Complete the chart with information from the article in Exercise 1. How much sleep, water, and exercise does the article recommend? What types of foods does it suggest?

	What the article recommends
sleep	
water	
exercise	
diet	

3 What are the results of doing what the article recommends?

	Results of doing what the article recommends
sleep	
water	
exercise	
diet	

4 How much sleep and exercise do you get? How much water do you drink? What types of foods do you eat? After reading the article in Exercise 1, is there anything that you would like to do differently? Why?

GRAMMAR EXPANDER

1 Answer the questions about your own personal care products. Write complete sentences with <u>some</u> or <u>any</u>.

1 Is there any soap in your bathroom?
   ....
2 Do you have some hand lotion in your bag?
   ....
3 Are you wearing any aftershave or perfume now?
   ....
4 Would you like some sunscreen?
   ....
5 Do you have any dental floss at home?
   ....

2 Read each pair of sentences. Which sentence is correct? Circle the letter.

1 a There isn't enough lotion.   b There isn't too many lotion.
2 a Did she use too many hairspray?   b Did she use too much hairspray?
3 a Do you have too much nail polish?   b Do you have too many nail polish?
4 a I don't have enough eye shadow.   b I don't have too many eye shadow.
5 a He has way too much razors.   b He has way too many razors.

3 Complete each sentence with <u>fewer</u> or <u>less</u>.

1 Which hair stylist has .... appointments today?
2 This bottle has .... shampoo in it than the other one.
3 With my new job, I have a lot .... time to put on makeup in the mornings.
4 I know a lot of people with tattoos, but .... people with pierced eyebrows.
5 You should wear .... makeup. Your skin is naturally beautiful.

UNIT 5 45

4 Complete each sentence with <u>something</u>, <u>anything</u>, <u>everything</u>, or <u>nothing</u>.

1 I don't know .... about hair transplants.
2 Do you need .... from the makeup counter?
3 .... can convince me to have cosmetic surgery.
4 There's .... interesting about a man with a shaved head.
5 I'd like an appointment for a massage. Do you have .... available this afternoon?
6 I thought we had toothpaste, but there's .... in the bathroom cabinet.
7 Dale doesn't like to eat or use .... that isn't organic.
8 I think there's .... in your hair. Oh, never mind. It's a cute hair clip.

WRITING HANDBOOK

1 Label the parts of the formal letter. Use the words in the box.

> complimentary close
> recipient's name
> recipient's position
> recipient's mailing address
> salutation
> sender's signature
> sender's full name
> sender's contact information
> the date

2 Read the letter to an advice column. Write a response, using your own opinion and making your own suggestions. Express your understanding of the person's problem. Include a salutation, a complimentary close, and your signature above your full name.

1 .... → 625 Harrison Boulevard
                                     Grapevine, Texas
2 .... e-mail: cclark101@gmail.com
3 .... → January 13, 2021

Everett Johnson, Manager   4 ....
Luxe Premiere Salon
3304 Broadway Blvd.   5 ....
Dallas, Texas
                           6 ....
Dear Mr. Johnson:
   I'm writing to let you know that I was very pleased with the service provided by the staff of the Luxe Premiere Salon when I was in Dallas last week. The manicurist was exceptional, and my hair stylist was very knowledgeable and extremely talented. She did a beautiful job with coloring my hair. I particularly enjoyed the relaxing music and the use of aromatherapy throughout the salon. Lavender is so refreshing. Finally, the prices were fair, the staff was very friendly, and I left the salon feeling great about myself and the day ahead.
   I want you to know that I am recommending Luxe Premiere Salon to all my friends and have told them that they should visit you even if they have to make a bit of a drive out of their way. I will definitely be scheduling future appointments at your amazing salon.

Sincerely,   7 ....
Celeste Clark   8 ....
Celeste Clark   9 ....

Dear Teens Anonymous,
   I have a problem with my 19-year-old daughter. She came back from college with this ridiculous tattoo on her ankle. I know she's an adult and can do what she wants, but we have a party for my mother's 80th birthday next weekend. Our family, especially my mother and father, is very conservative. They will get angry when they see the tattoo and it will ruin the party. I asked my daughter to wear long pants to hide her tattoo, but she refused. She says lots of people have them and it's not a big deal. I told her if she won't cover her tattoo, then she isn't invited to the party. Now she won't speak to me. What should I do?

Sincerely yours,
Darcy in Denver

UNIT 6 Eating Well

Warm-up

1 Look at the pictures. What do you think the people are saying? Use the words from the box.

| addict | can't stand | ~~crazy about~~ | don't care for | love |

1 I'm crazy about chocolate!
2 ....
3 ....
4 ....
5 ....

2 What class of food does each food item belong to? Use the words from the box to complete the chart.

| beans   berries   cheese   eggs   green vegetables   meats   melons   milk
milk-based desserts   nuts and seeds   poultry   red and orange vegetables   refined grains
seafood   soy products   starchy vegetables   whole grains   yogurt |

Dairy Foods	Fruits	Grains	Protein Foods	Vegetables

3 Answer the questions. Circle all the correct food items.

1 Which of these are fruits?
   a berries   b beans   c poultry   d melons   e eggs

2 Which of these are NOT vegetables?
   a potatoes   b whole grains   c carrots   d yogurt   e nuts and seeds

3 Which of these are protein foods?
   a brown rice b cheese   c eggs   d seafood   e meats

4 Which of these are whole or refined grains?
   a pasta   b white bread   c potatoes   d nuts   e beans

UNIT 6   47

4 Match the sentences on the left to the explanations on the right. Write the letter.

.... 1 I wonder what's going on.
.... 2 I couldn't live without it.
.... 3 I feel a little guilty about it.
.... 4 I'm cutting down on it.
.... 5 I'm giving it up.
.... 6 I'm on a diet.

a You're going to stop eating a certain thing.
b You're decreasing consumption of something.
c You've changed eating habits to lose weight.
d You feel bad about doing something.
e You don't know what's happening.
f It's impossible for you to give something up.

LESSON 1

1 Look at the pictures. Complete the reasons for declining food.

1 I'm on a ....
I'm trying to ....

2 I don't eat beef. It's
....

3 I'm ....
sugar.

4 I don't ....
broccoli.

5 This burger doesn't
.... me.

6 I'm ....
chocolate.

2 Complete the conversation with phrases from the box.

| against her religion   doesn't care for   is allergic to   is avoiding   is on a diet |

A: I want to have a small dinner party on Saturday. Can you help me prepare the menu?

B: Sure. Remember that my brother **(1)** .... , so we can't make anything too fatty. Why don't we make some chicken?

A: I would, but Anika can't eat meat. It's **(2)** .... Maybe I can make my rice dish.

B: I don't know. Marty is trying to eat healthy, so he **(3)** .... white rice.

A: OK . . . Then how about black bean soup with peppers?

B: I don't think Austin would like that. He **(4)** .... spicy food.

A: You're right. Is there anything that everyone can eat?

B: Hmm . . . I don't know, but I hope you'll make that delicious coconut cream pie for dessert!

A: I can't. Remember, Ethan **(5)** .... coconut!

B: I have an idea. Why don't we just go out to eat? Then everyone can order what they want.

48   UNIT 6

3 Complete the statements with a food or drink to describe your own food preferences.

1 I'm avoiding ....
2 I don't care for ....
3 I'm not crazy about ....
4 I'm not much of a .... drinker.
5 .... doesn't / don't agree with me.

4 Complete each negative yes / no question.

1 A: .... that a delicious meal?
   B: Yes, it definitely was.
2 A: .... you just love kale?
   B: No, I don't really care for it.
3 A: .... you going to order dessert?
   B: No, I'm trying to lose weight.
4 A: .... this trail mix delicious?
   B: Actually, I didn't have any. I'm allergic to nuts.
5 A: .... Dylan stop eating meat?
   B: Yes, he did. He is trying a plant-based diet.
6 A: .... that soup have enough salt in it already?
   B: It probably does, but I'm a little bit of a salt addict.

5 Complete each negative yes / no question. Use the words in parentheses.

1 A: .... seafood? (she / like)
   B: No, she completely avoids it.
2 A: .... on that pizza? (there / be / pineapple)
   B: Yes, there is. Do you have a problem with that?
3 A: .... sushi before? (he / ever / try)
   B: No, he hasn't. We should order some.
4 A: .... on a diet all summer? (you / be)
   B: Yes, I have. I lost some weight, but I'm so hungry.
5 A: .... the casserole I made? (you / like)
   B: I liked it very much. I just couldn't eat any more.
6 A: .... dinner in tonight? (we / order)
   B: Yes, we are. Thanks for the reminder. I'll call them now.

6 Choose the correct response. Write the letter on the line.

.... 1 "I'm a coffee addict. What about you?"
.... 2 "Don't you eat meat?"
.... 3 "I'll pass on the cake."
.... 4 "I'm sorry. I didn't know you were on a diet."
.... 5 "Please, help yourself."

a Actually, no. It's against my religion.
b Don't you eat sweets?
c No worries.
d Thank you. Everything looks so good.
e Actually, I'm a big tea drinker.

UNIT 6 49

LESSON 2

1 Complete each sentence with <u>used to</u> or <u>use to</u> and the verb in parentheses. Use contractions when possible.

1 I ....*didn't use to worry*........ about eating too much sugar or salt. (not / worry)
2 Before I was an adult, I .... very many vegetables. (not like)
3 Daisy .... meat, but now she's a vegetarian. (eat)
4 Aaron .... sweets after every meal. (have) But he's avoiding sugars now.
5 I .... a lot of soda. (drink) But I'm giving it up to cut calories.
6 .... you .... a lot of creamer in your coffee? (put)

2 Circle the correct words to complete the sentences.

1 When I was young, I (didn't use to / didn't used to) like tomatoes.
2 None of my friends (use to / used to) have laptops. Now, we all do.
3 Sarah (used to be / use to was) a vegan, but she's trying a new diet.
4 I (didn't use to / used to) drink a lot of water, but now I do.
5 (Did you used to / Didn't you use to) go out more before you had children?

3 Read about Emilee's food passions. Then complete each sentence with <u>used to</u> or <u>didn't use to</u> and the verb in parentheses.

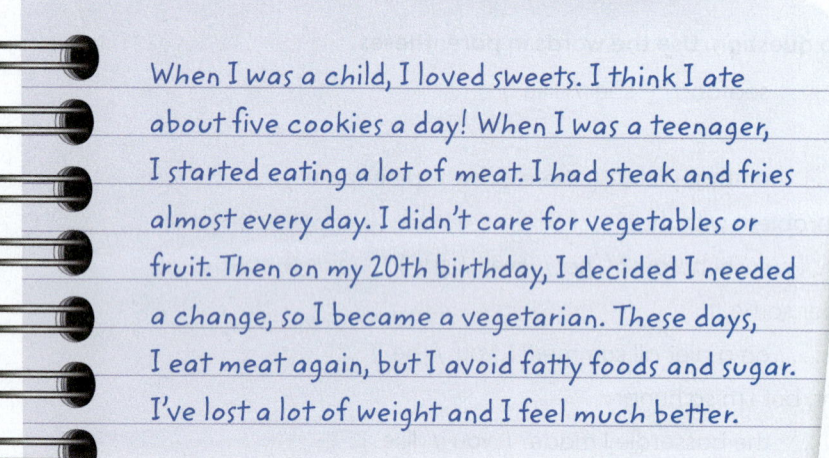

> When I was a child, I loved sweets. I think I ate about five cookies a day! When I was a teenager, I started eating a lot of meat. I had steak and fries almost every day. I didn't care for vegetables or fruit. Then on my 20th birthday, I decided I needed a change, so I became a vegetarian. These days, I eat meat again, but I avoid fatty foods and sugar. I've lost a lot of weight and I feel much better.

Emilee

1 When Emilee was young, she .... a lot of sweets, but now she avoids sugar. (eat)
2 As a teenager, she .... steak and fries a lot. (have)
3 Before she turned 20, she .... vegetables. (like)
4 Emilee .... a vegetarian, but now she eats meat again. (be)
5 She .... care of herself, but now she eats well and feels better. (take)

4 How have your eating habits and tastes changed? Write four sentences. Use <u>use to</u> or <u>used to</u>.

1 .... *I used to be a coffee addict, but now I avoid it* ....
2 ....
3 ....
4 ....
5 ....

5 Complete the conversation with phrases from the box. Not all of the phrases will be used.

| be crazy about | can't stand | eat peaches | lost my taste for |
| my favorite | No way | those peaches | used to eat |

A: Just look at (1) .... Don't they look delicious?

B: They do look good. But I don't (2) .... anymore.

A: Really? Don't you like them?

B: Actually, I used to (3) .... them. I can't explain it, but one day, I just
(4) .... them.

A: (5) .... ! I couldn't live without them. They're
(6) .... fruit.

LESSON 3

1 Match the news headline on the left to the reason for adopting a diet on the right. Write the letter.

.... 1 Top Ten Ways to Boost Your Immunity and Prevent Serious Illness   **a** to lose weight
.... 2 Looking to Drop a Few Pounds? Start Each Day with This Drink!   **b** to gain weight
.... 3 Exercise and Diet Are Keys to Feeling Good and Living a Long Life   **c** to protect the environment
.... 4 Need to Bulk Up and Put on Some Pounds? Here's How.   **d** to avoid disease
.... 5 Meatless Burgers Taste Good and Save Lives   **e** to avoid killing animals
.... 6 New Food Processing Technique Minimizes Effect on Climate   **f** to stay healthy

2 What is each person's reason for adopting a specific diet? Circle the correct answer.

1 Evan avoids foods that are high in sugar, salt, and fat. She prefers foods that are more natural and have a lot of nutrients, like green vegetables. (to stay healthy / to lose weight / to gain weight)

2 My wife and I used to eat a lot of red meat and way too many sweets. Our doctor was concerned about my heart. He thought I might get sick. Now, we try to eat healthier, low-fat foods more regularly. (to avoid killing animals / to avoid disease / to lose weight)

3 Todd was training for a marathon, but he let himself get too thin. He wasn't eating or drinking enough. He weighs less than he should for his height. He's starting to include more dairy and protein in his diet. (to protect the environment / to lose weight / to gain weight)

4 The nurse told Bella that she weighs too much. She put her on a low-fat diet and encouraged her to walk more frequently. A better diet plus exercise should help her see a difference. (to lose weight / to gain weight / to avoid disease)

3 Read the article. Which statement about meat alternatives would the author probably agree with? Circle the correct answer.

a They have improved enough to have future success.

b They have improved but future success is unlikely.

c They will only have future success if their quality is further improved.

New on the Menu: Plant-Based Meat Alternatives

For years, plant-based meat alternatives sat lonely on supermarket shelves. They were made of vegetables, beans, and grains, and their market was mainly vegans and vegetarians, who make up only three percent of food shoppers. In recent years, however, a range of new products that look and taste much more like meat (but aren't) have appeared, and they're already doing much better than the older versions.

These new meat alternatives have been mainly designed to attract meat eaters in the global market who are interested in including new vegetarian options in their diet. They are prepared through complex processes and contain long lists of ingredients that include more than just vegetables. The final products aim to taste just like chicken, beef, or other natural meats. Many reviewers say they look and smell like meat. They cost about the same, too. Meat eaters say that these products are nearly or even as good as some real meat products, but they can still tell the difference.

In the food service industry, global fast-food and other restaurant chains have added plant-based meat alternatives to their menus. Burgers, hot dogs, tacos, and pizza made with plant-based beef, sausage, and chicken have become popular items, and partnerships between restaurants and meat alternative companies have been very successful. Sales of these meat alternatives set records last year, and the companies earned huge profits, which they are investing in hiring more staff and increasing production facilities.

There are many other signs that plant-based meat alternatives will have a promising future. Concern for the natural environment often affects customer choices, and these alternatives claim to be more environmentally friendly than meat. Also, meat production around the world is increasing, which means the market for meat alternatives will likely increase as well. The market for meat is growing particularly quickly in India and China, and a recent survey of residents of those enormous nations indicated significant interest in plant-based meat alternatives. Finally, strong evidence for the success of these new foods comes from the meat industry itself: many meat producers are starting their own lines of plant-based meat alternatives.

4 Reread the article in Exercise 3. Complete the sentences. Circle the correct words.

1 Earlier plant-based meat alternatives were bought mainly by people who (used to eat / didn't eat / usually ate) meat.

2 New plant-based meat alternatives are mainly aimed at (vegans / vegetarians / meat eaters).

3 The new plant-based meat alternatives have more (ingredients / vegetables / meats) than the older ones.

4 A lot of people think that the new plant-based meat alternatives taste (almost as good as / exactly like / very little like) meat.

5 Plant-based meat alternative companies have formed partnerships with (supermarkets / meat producers / restaurants).

6 The growing demand for meat will (harm / help / not affect) the demand for plant-based meat alternatives.

7 Plant-based meat alternative producers claim their products are (more delicious / less expensive / less harmful to the environment) than actual meat.

52   UNIT 6

5 Review the article in Exercise 3 again. Match the words from the article with their definitions. Draw a line.

1. alternative
2. environmentally friendly
3. ingredient
4. invest
5. promising
6. version

a. something that can be used instead of the actual thing
b. likely to be good or successful
c. to use time, effort, or money to improve something to help it succeed
d. one of the things you use to make a particular food
e. not damaging the environment
f. a form of something that has been changed a little from another form

LESSON 4

1 Complete the postcard with the correct form of <u>taste</u>, <u>smell</u>, or <u>look</u>.

Hi Omar,

I'm having a great time in Marrakech! Yesterday, I walked in the main square, and it _____(1) like a scene from a movie! People in long, beautiful robes were everywhere, and there was so much food! I saw some fish that _____(2) like the kind we have at home. Somewhere else in the market, I couldn't see where, there was a kind of grilled meat that _____(3) wonderful. I found it but didn't know if I should try it. It _____(4) kind of strange, but I bought some anyway. It was delicious! It _____(5) both spicy and sweet. It wasn't at all what I expected! You should come here on your next vacation!

See you soon,
Amina

2 Complete the word webs. Write three examples of foods that match each adjective.

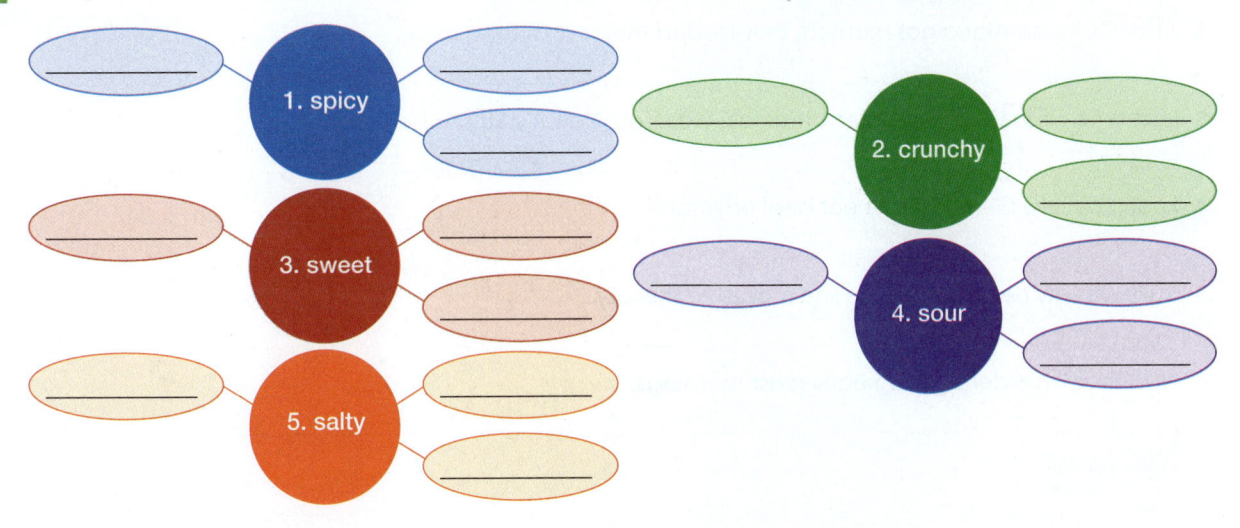

1. spicy
2. crunchy
3. sweet
4. sour
5. salty

UNIT 6   53

3 Describe an unusual dish you have tried. Where and when did you eat it? What did it look, smell, and taste like? Would you recommend it to someone or not?

One of the strangest things I've ever eaten is . . .

DID YOU KNOW . . . ?
There are more than 1,400 different species of insects that are eaten for food around the world. The most popular are crickets, grasshoppers, grubs, ants, bees, and caterpillars. One health benefit: insects are low in fat and high in protein!

GRAMMAR EXPANDER

1 Complete the conversations. Complete the negative <u>yes</u> / <u>no</u> questions and write short answers.

1 A: ......*Don't*...... you like spicy food?
  B: ......*No, I don't*...... . It doesn't agree with me.
2 A: .... you on a diet?
  B: .... I've lost five pounds already.
3 A: .... Courtney eat meat?
  B: .... She's not a big fan.
4 A: .... Michael allergic to chocolate?
  B: .... , but he still eats a piece now and then.
5 A: .... those seedless grapes taste great?
  B: .... I love grapes!

2 Read the statements about a habitual action that is no longer true today. Then rewrite the information as a single sentence with <u>use to</u> or <u>used to</u>.

1 As Cybil got older, her tastes changed. Now she actually likes asparagus.
....

2 After Colt and Alana got married, they traded their car in for a truck.
....

3 Last time we were at this hotel, breakfast was free. Now it's $8 per person.
....

4 I can't believe Gerry doesn't eat beef anymore!
....

5 Sally was my neighbor before she moved to the city.
....

6 Now that I'm older, I get up early most mornings.
....

54   UNIT 6

3 Write a yes / no question for each response, using a form of used to.

1 **A:** ....
  B: No, they didn't. This many restaurants didn't use to deliver takeout orders.

2 **A:** ....
  B: No, they didn't. TVs didn't use to be so big.

3 **A:** ....
  B: Yes, he did. Fernando used to live closer to his office.

4 **A:** ....
  B: No, she didn't. Gisselle didn't use to eat a lot of fish. But she does now.

5 **A:** ....
  B: Yes, she did. She used to love chocolate. She's still crazy about it.

6 **A:** ....
  B: No, I didn't. I didn't use to have a smartphone when I was your age.

7 **A:** ....
  B: No, they didn't. People didn't use to read the news online.

4 Complete the affirmative or negative sentences with be used to. Use contractions.

1 Troy colored his beard. It was gray and now it's red. He .... it yet.
2 I .... my husband's cooking now. I .... that much salt before.
3 We .... sweet desserts, but we love my cousin's Lemon Yogurt Cake.
4 She .... avoiding sugars and fatty foods. It's part of her diet.
5 Carlito borrowed his brother's truck, but he usually drives a compact two-door car. He
  .... driving such a big truck.
6 Karen just got a haircut. It's very different from her old style. She .... her new look yet.
7 I .... budget hotels, so it's a treat to stay in this expensive hotel with so many amenities.

5 Complete the statements in your own way.

1 Carson use to eat a lot of pasta, but she recently discovered that she has a gluten allergy. She's getting used to ....

2 Edgar's family recently moved from North Carolina to California. They can't get used to ....
  ....

3 Eva's doctor told her she needed to start eating better and exercising. She's working hard on planning healthier meals. She still hasn't gotten used to ....
  ....

UNIT 6

6 Write three sentences about things you did often when you were a child. Use <u>would</u>.

> When I was a child, I would play soccer all day on Saturdays.

1.
2.
3.

WRITING HANDBOOK

1 Circle the best subordinating conjunction to complete each sentence.

1 (If / Since / Though) Vivian doesn't care for fish or seafood, we didn't go out for sushi.
2 You'll love the buffet at Perry's Steakhouse (unless / if / because) you're a vegetarian.
3 It's important to eat fruits and vegetables every day (because / unless / although) they are great sources of vitamins and fiber.
4 On the Atkins Diet, you can eat butter (since / even though / unless) it has a lot of fat.
5 (Though / If / Unless) you drink a lot of coffee in the evening, you won't sleep well.
6 We prefer to stay at bed and breakfasts (because / though / unless) they're very comfortable and the food is usually good.
7 (Unless / Though / Because) it's difficult to completely change your eating habits, you can succeed by making one small change at a time.
8 (Because / Unless / Since) I'm at a dinner party, I usually don't eat dessert.
9 You should avoid fatty foods and sweets (unless / even though / if) you're watching your weight.
10 (Since / Although / If) I want to stay healthy, I still occasionally splurge on sweets, especially chocolate.

2 Write two paragraphs about your eating habits. In the first paragraph, write about your diet. In the second paragraph, write about how healthy you think your diet is and what you could do to improve it. Use the questions as a guide. Use four different subordinating conjunctions.

> I'm a big meat eater. I couldn't live without steak! Even though I love the taste, coffee doesn't agree with me . . .

Questions
What are your food passions?
What foods could you not live without?
Are there any foods that you avoid?
How many servings of each food group do you eat each day?
Have you ever tried to change what you eat? Why or why not?

UNIT 7 Driving Around

Warm-up

1 Look at the pictures. Write the dangerous driving habit.

1 .... while driving

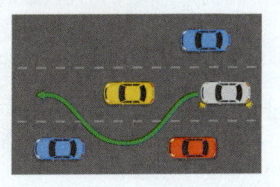

2 .... through traffic

3 not .... when turning

4 not .... at red lights

5 ....

6 .... on the phone

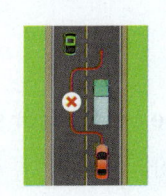

7 .... in a no-passing zone

8 ....

2 Circle the correct answer to complete each sentence.

1 Can you believe that driver? She has her cellphone in her hand, and she's (passing / texting / signaling) while driving. That's so dangerous!

2 Wow! That driver is going way too fast. I hope he slows down. He really shouldn't (speed / pass / stop). There's a school crossing up ahead.

3 Slow down! That driver in front of you is about to turn left, but she isn't (signaling / talking on her phone / speeding).

4 That driver behind us is way too close to us. I hope I don't have to stop quickly! Why do people (weave / pass / tailgate) like that?

3 Complete each sentence with a bad driving habit from the box. Use the -ing form of each verb.

| not signal | tailgate | talk on the phone | text | speed |

1 The person in front of me suddenly hit his breaks. Now he's turning right but he's .... I almost ran into him!

2 She's going 60 miles per hour in a construction zone. I can't believe she's .... when people are working near the road.

3 I was driving on the highway when a truck quickly came up behind me. It was inches from my bumper. .... is so dangerous!

4 I was so nervous driving next to that blue sports car this morning. The guy was looking down at his phone and was obviously .... someone.

UNIT 7   57

4 Complete each statement. Circle the letter.

1. If a car has suddenly driven directly in front of you, it has ....
   a cut you off   b stopped cold

2. If you've had a minor accident in your car, you've had a ....
   a crash   b fender bender

3. If something was easy to handle, you'd say it was ....
   a a fender bender   b no big deal

4. If your car suddenly dies, you might say it ....
   a stopped cold   b cut you off

5. When you are leaving somewhere in your car, you might .... a parking space.
   a pull out of   b stop next to

> **DID YOU KNOW…?**
> Sending or reading a text takes your eyes off the road for a total of five seconds. If you are driving at 55 mph (88 kph), that is like traveling the length of a soccer field with your eyes closed.

LESSON 1

1 Look at each picture. Write the correct car system or part from the box.

| the battery   the brakes   the engine   the motor   the steering |

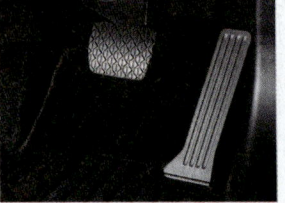

1 ....
2 .... 
3 .... 
4 .... 

2 Complete the sentences with the correct car system or part.

1. Last night, I had a hard time stopping my car at the traffic light. .... were making a very loud noise and I had to push the pedal all the way to the floor. It was scary.

2. Tara left her lights on last night after driving home from work. Now her car won't start. We think it's probably a problem with ....

3. For some reason, I can't turn left in my car. I can only turn right. Something is definitely wrong with ....

4. Virgil was driving to work and his car started making noise and smoking. It suddenly quit as he was pulling over to the side of the road. That's not good. I hope .... is okay.

58   UNIT 7

3 Complete the sentences. Circle the correct answers.

1 My daughter (**'s been studying** / studying) for her driver's test.
2 Cassidy's has been (had / **having**) a lot of car trouble recently.
3 My car has (**needed** / needs) new brakes for weeks.
4 We (are driving / **'ve been driving**) for hours. Aren't we there yet?
5 Francisco (**had** / has been having) a fender bender yesterday.
6 He (**'s been wanting** / 's wanted) a new truck for years.
7 She has (**believed** / been believing) for years that the future belongs to electric vehicles.
8 My mechanic (told / **has been telling**) me for a while that my car isn't going to last much longer, so I need to buy another.

4 Complete the conversations. Write the correct present perfect continuous form of the verb in parentheses. Use contractions when possible.

1 **A:** How will he decide what kind of car to buy?
   B: Well, _he's been doing_ a lot of research. (he / do)
2 **A:** .... about getting a minivan ever since you had the baby. (you / talk)
   B: Well, I'm finally going to do it.
3 **A:** Are you going to buy a convertible?
   B: .... about it. (I / think)
4 **A:** I heard your son was advising you on your search for a new car.
   B: Yes. .... to talk me into buying a plug-in car. (he / try)
5 **A:** Why did you take away your daughter's car keys?
   B: .... while driving. (she / text) That's so dangerous!
6 **A:** Are you planning to rent a car for your road trip?
   B: Yes. .... at Jeep Wranglers. (we / look)
7 **A:** Can Everett and Anna afford a new car this year?
   B: I think so. .... money aside all year. (they / put)
8 **A:** .... that same car for twelve years. (Grace / drive)
   B: I know. She sure knows how to be frugal.
9 **A:** .... the same brand of car since 1982. (I / buy)
   B: What a loyal customer you are!

5 Put the conversation in order. Write the number on the line.

_1_ **A:** I was on my way home from the store yesterday, and the car just died.
..... **B:** We've been having brake trouble and the car is making strange noises.
..... **A:** Really? Why?
..... **B:** No way! What was wrong?
..... **A:** That's no fun. What kind of car are you going to get?
..... **B:** You know, we've been thinking of getting a new one, too.
..... **A:** The engine. Again! Enough is enough. It's time for a new car.
..... **B:** Probably a compact car. It's just the two of us now.

UNIT 7

LESSON 2

1 Look at each picture. Circle the correct sentence that describes the accident.

1. a They hit a tree.
   b They had a head-on collision.
   c There was a pileup.

2. a He sideswiped a parked car.
   b He rear-ended another car.
   c He hit a tree.

3. a She sideswiped a parked car.
   b There was a pileup.
   c She had a head-on collision.

4. a They had a collision.
   b They hit a tree.
   c There was a pileup.

5. a We had a head-on collision.
   b We sideswiped a parked car.
   c We rear-ended another car.

6. a They hit a tree.
   b There was a pileup.
   c It was a head-on collision.

2 Match the sentences that describe the same traffic accident. Write the correct letter.

.... 1 There was a big accident on the highway. Multiple cars were involved.
.... 2 I had an accident. I hit another car.
.... 3 I was trying to park my car when I hit another car's door.
.... 4 My car hit a bump, swerved off the road, and ran into a tree.
.... 5 I lost control and drove straight into the front of that other car.
.... 6 I drove into the back of another car.

a I rear-ended a car.
b I had a head-on collision.
c I had a collision.
d I hit a tree.
e There was a pile-up.
f I sideswiped a car.

3 Complete the conversation. Use the past continuous or simple past tense form of the verbs in parentheses.

A: Hi Blanca. What's wrong?

B: I **(1)** .... a car accident on the way home from work today. (have)

A: Oh, no! What **(2)** .... ? (happen)

B: Well, I **(3)** .... (drive) down the highway when my brother **(4)** .... (call) me. He **(5)** .... (ask) what I **(6)** .... (do), and I **(7)** .... (tell) him I was driving and would call him back later. But he had a funny story to tell me and couldn't wait. Anyway, by the end of the story, I **(8)** .... (laugh) so hard I couldn't see. That's when I **(9)** .... (drive) into a stop sign.

4 Choose the correct response. Write the letter on the line.

..... 1 I got into an accident today.
..... 2 Are you OK?
..... 3 How did it happen?
..... 4 Luckily, I was wearing my seat belt.
..... 5 Was there much damage?

a The other driver wasn't paying attention and he backed into my car.
b Not really. The other guy will have to replace a taillight.
c Yes, I'm fine. It was just a fender bender.
d Thank goodness.
e Oh, no!

5 Have you or someone you know ever had an accident? What happened? Write a note to a friend about it. Include past continuous and simple past tense in your description.

LESSON 3

1 Complete the conversations with the correct phrasal verbs from the box.

drop off   fill out   fill up   pick out   pick up

1 **A:** You need to .... a dress from this collection.
  B: But they are all so pretty. I don't know which one to choose.
2 **A:** When will you .... the rent check?
  B: I'll bring it by on my way home from work.

3 **A:** We need to .... on healthy foods before we go to the party.
  B: You're right. We'll eat too many sweets if we're hungry.
4 **A:** Be sure to .... the application form completely.
  B: I will. I really want this job.
5 **A:** When can I .... the car?
  B: You can come get it tomorrow morning.

2 Circle the correct phrasal verbs to complete the paragraph.

  I recently went on vacation with my husband to the Florida Keys. Before we flew in, we decided to rent a car. It was a very easy process. First, we had to **(1)** (fill out / fill up / pick out) an online form. Next, we had to **(2)** (pick up / fill up / pick out) the vehicle we wanted. There were so many to choose from. We chose a red sports car for fun. When we arrived in Florida, we went to the car rental desk to **(3)** (fill out / drop off / pick up) the car keys. The lady at the desk told us that the car had a full tank of gas, but she reminded us that we would need to **(4)** (drop off / fill up / fill out) the tank before bringing the car back. She also said we could **(5)** (drop off / pick out / pick up) they keys at the kiosk in the airport on our way out so it wouldn't take a lot of our time. Finally, we were on our way.

LESSON 4

1 Read the Golden Rules of Safe Driving. Complete the statements with words from the box.

flash   gesture   honk   maintain   observe   pay

The Golden Rules of Safe Driving

RULE 1: Don't eat, text, or talk on your cell phone when you're driving. Keep your eyes on the road and always **(1)** _____ attention.

RULE 2: It's important to **(2)** _____ the speed limit and **(3)** _____ a safe distance behind the car in front of you.

RULE 3: Expect to get stuck in traffic. When you do, be patient. Don't **(4)** _____ your horn, and never **(5)** _____ at other drivers with your fist or stare at them. It doesn't help. In fact, it usually makes things worse!

RULE 4: Be careful at night. Many people drive more slowly, so don't be aggressive. Find a safe place to pass, but never **(6)** _____ your lights.

2 Look at the pictures. Complete the sentences to describe the driving behavior.

1 Bad or aggressive drivers .... other drivers.

2 Good drivers observe the ....

3 Bad or aggressive drivers .... their ....

4 Good drivers pay ....

5 Bad or aggressive drivers flash .... at other drivers.

6 Good drivers maintain a safe ....

7 Bad or aggressive drivers .... at other drivers.

3 Do you know someone who is a bad driver? Why do you think so? Describe the person's driving habits.

_____
_____
_____
_____
_____

4 Read the online message board. What experience have all three drivers had? Circle the correct answer.

a They all had an accident.
b They all were in a dangerous situation.
c They all failed the test to get their license.

The Driver's Point of View

File Edit Links Tools Help Chat

Whether you're a beginner or long-time driver, we're interested in your experiences on the road. Post yours below!

Rich92 I recently took a new friend on a dinner date. I wanted her to have a wonderful time, so I rented a car. Since I'm not a very good driver, I always rent a compact car because they're easy to drive. But when I got to the car rental agency, all they had left was a giant pick-up truck. It was too late to change plans, so I took it. I don't know how I got to the restaurant and back without an accident. I almost sideswiped half a dozen cars! I thought she'd never want to see me again, but when I dropped her off, she said I drove a pick-up really well and asked me to help her move a sofa the next day!
👍 Reply

88Rules I had a difficult time getting my driver's license. In fact, I failed the road test two times before passing. All three times, I had the same examiner. The first time, I sideswiped a parked car. The second time was worse. I hit a tree, and the examiner was slightly injured. When he saw me before my third test, he looked really nervous and stressed out. While we were driving, he kept wiping his forehead with a handkerchief. But when the test was finally over, he suddenly relaxed, smiled from ear to ear, and shouted, "Congratulations!"
👍 Reply

Drive01 One day, I was following the directions on my phone while driving to a friend's house that I'd never visited before. It was getting dark when I turned onto a dirt road. Soon, a car behind me started honking its horn. I thought maybe I was driving too slowly, so I sped up. Then, the car started flashing its lights. I stopped, and so did the other car. The driver said, "Didn't you see the sign? It says "Bridge Out." The bridge up ahead was damaged by a storm last week. Cars still can't cross it. You'll need to go the long way." I thanked her for saving my life. I'm more careful now when I follow directions on my phone.
👍 Reply

5 Read the messages in Exercise 4 again. Which drivers are the statements about? Check (✓) all correct answers.

	Rich92	88Rules	Drive01
1 The driver probably doesn't drive very often.	☐	☐	☐
2 The driver had a traffic accident.	☐	☐	☐
3 The driver had a passenger.	☐	☐	☐
4 The driver had to change the route along the way.	☐	☐	☐
5 Someone said that the driver drove well.	☐	☐	☐
6 Someone warned the driver about danger.	☐	☐	☐

6 Read the messages in Exercise 4 again. Answer the questions with information from the messages.

1 Why did Rich92's date ask him to move her sofa?
....

2 Why was 88Rules' examiner nervous during the road test?
....

3 Why didn't Drive01 know that the bridge was damaged?
....

GRAMMAR EXPANDER

1 Complete the conversations. Write yes / no or information questions with the verb in the present perfect continuous.

1 **A:** .... for the past six years?
   B: I've been living in Brazil.

2 **A:** .... on your car?
   B: They've been working on it for two hours.

3 **A:** .... at the lodge?
   B: Yes, I have been enjoying my stay.

4 **A:** .... ?
   B: She's been working at the local library.

5 **A:** .... since your accident?
   B: Mostly, I've been resting and recovering.

2 Complete the statements. Use the present participle of the verb in parentheses.

1 My car is .... a strange sound. (make)
2 That boy is .... while driving. (text)
3 Everyone is .... their horns. (honk)
4 I am .... a safe distance from other cars. (maintain)
5 Francisco is .... to the grocery store. (go)
6 She is .... the other car go around her. (let)

3 Complete each sentence in your own way. Use the past continuous or the simple past tense.

1 They were having breakfast when ....
2 While ...., it started to snow.
3 He had an accident when ....
4 While Garrett was making dinner, Gene ....
5 When ...., Caitlan was leaving her house.

64 UNIT 7

WRITING HANDBOOK

1 Insert commas where necessary in the following sentences.
1. Gabby was texting on her phone changing lanes and gesturing at other drivers.
2. You should put on your seatbelt and adjust your mirrors before you pull out.
3. My brother has three vehicles: a truck a convertible and a mini-van.
4. They plan to drive from Denton to Greenwood a three-hour road trip and stay overnight.
5. Dillon likes driving sports cars and really big pick-up trucks.

2 Combine each pair of sentences into one sentence. Use two independent clauses and use **and**.
1. My mapping app isn't working. I think we're lost.
   ....
2. The driver was putting on makeup. She hit the car in front of her.
   ....
3. My sister loves fast cars. She gets to test drive them at her job at the Speedway.
   ....
4. I was backing out of the garage. I hit a tree.
   ....

3 Complete the statements with your own ideas. Add commas.
1. I'm traveling to a city without good public transportation. Therefore ....
   ....
2. To find a good rate on a rental car, check travel and car rental agency websites. In addition ....
   ....
3. Small children must usually sit in the back seat of a car. Furthermore ....
   ....

4 Write a letter to your city government. Suggest ways that the city can make driving safer. Use the questions as a guide. Connect words and sentences with **and**, **in addition**, **furthermore**, and **therefore**.

> Dear Sir or Madam,
>   I am writing about a big problem in our city. A lot of drivers don't pay attention. Furthermore, they …

Ideas
What are some problems that drivers experience in your area?
What are the causes of these problems?
What dangerous driving habits are common?
How can these problems be fixed?
How can the government encourage good driving behavior?

UNIT 7

UNIT 8 Doing the Right Thing

Warm-up

1 Read the messages to an advice column. What advice do you think Amanda will give? Check the box.

---

1. Dear Amanda:
I bought five video games this morning at the store. The clerk only charged me for three. I didn't say anything at the time. Should I return to the store and offer to pay for the other two games?
Sammi   Reply 7h   [Click here for Amanda's advice]

2. Dear Amanda:
Yesterday, I saw someone get on the free airport shuttle bus at my hotel. I know he wasn't staying there. Should I tell the hotel manager?
Gretel   Reply 8h   [Click here for Amanda's advice]

3. Dear Amanda:
My favorite lipstick had the wrong price on it. It was half the usual price, so I bought six of them. Do you think that's OK?
Hannah   Reply 11h   [Click here for Amanda's advice]

4. Dear Amanda:
I reserved a compact rental car, but when I went to pick it up, they gave me a luxury car for the same price. Should I tell them that they made a mistake?
Patrick   Reply 18h   [Click here for Amanda's advice]

---

1. ☐ Sammi should tell someone at the store that she wasn't charged for two of the video games.
   ☐ Sammi should just relax and enjoy the games without saying anything.
2. ☐ Gretel should tell the hotel manager about the person using the shuttle bus.
   ☐ Gretel should mind her own business and not complain about someone else.
3. ☐ Hannah should feel great about saving money.
   ☐ Hannah should go back and tell the store manager the price was wrong and pay the correct price.
4. ☐ Patrick should tell the rental company they made a mistake and offer to pay the difference.
   ☐ Patrick should stop worrying and enjoy his luxury car.

2 Have you ever experienced a moral dilemma similar to the ones described in Exercise 1? Write a letter to Amanda about your situation.

3 Match the language on the left with its meaning on the right. Write the correct letter.

.... 1 a dead giveaway   a considered to be perfect
.... 2 Cut it out.   b reveals a fact or intention
.... 3 gossiping about someone   c Stop doing that.
.... 4 Why so glum?   d Why are you feeling down?
.... 5 can do no wrong   e support yourself in a difficult situation
.... 6 That person's no help.   f talking about someone who isn't present
.... 7 plays favorites   g doesn't do anything to fix the problem
.... 8 Stand up for yourself.   h treats some people better than others

LESSON 1

1 Match the sentences with the correct picture. Write the letter of the picture on the line.

.... 1 That milkshake is theirs.
.... 2 Hey! This donut is mine!
.... 3 Whose backpack is that?
.... 4 Oh, no! Whose bear is this?
.... 5 Excuse me? Is this phone yours?
.... 6 Uh-oh. I think this wallet is his.
.... 7 My goodness! Are all these mine?

2 Complete the conversations. Circle the correct words.

1 **A:** Excuse me, (is that yours? / that's mine. / that's yours.)
   B: Oh, sorry! It looks just like my raincoat.

2 **A:** (Whose ring is this? / I think this ring is hers. / Hey! That ring is mine!)
   B: Do you see that woman by the door? I think (it's mine. / it's his. / it's hers.)

3 **A:** I found this notebook. (Whose is it? / Is it yours? / I think it's his.)
   B: No. (It's mine. / Is it mine? / I think it's his.) He seems to be looking for it.

UNIT 8   67

3 Circle the correct words to complete the sentences.

1 Whose sunglasses are these, his or (**yours** / your)?
2 Those chips at the counter must be (our / **ours**).
3 She took the books back home because they were (**hers** / her).
4 (**Our** / Ours) flight leaves in two hours.
5 Which of these bags are (**his** / he's)?
6 Your phone is much nicer than (my / **mine**).

4 Rewrite each sentence using a possessive pronoun.

1 The hair spray is Audra's. *The hair spray is hers.*
2 The shampoo is everyone's. ....
3 The shaving cream is Clint's. ....
4 The toothbrushes are Caitlin's and Brock's. ....
5 The razors are Clint's. ....

5 Look at the pictures. Complete the conversations with possessive adjectives or possessive pronouns.

1 Isn't that phone .... ?
2 No, it isn't. It must be ....
3 Is this .... ?
4 No, it's not .... It's .... tip.

68 UNIT 8

6 Write the sentences in the correct order to make a conversation. Use the sentences in the box. Not all sentences will be used.

> Excuse me? Sir? Is this phone yours?
> Excuse me. Whose phone is this?
> My pleasure.
> No, it's not mine.
> No problem. Here you go.
> Thanks so much. That's really nice of you.
> Yes, it is! I can't believe I left it behind.

1 A: ....
2 B: ....
3 A: ....
4 B: ....
5 A: ....

DID YOU KNOW . . . ?
. . . 50% of people report losing something at least once a week?
Top 5 Lost Items:
1. phone
2. umbrella
3. bag / backpack
4. clothing
5. headphones

LESSON 2

1 Match the two parts of each conditional sentence. Write the letter on the line.

...... 1 If you go to my hairdresser, she'll . . .
...... 2 Grace would look great if she . . .
...... 3 If you find a wallet, you . . .
...... 4 If I knew whose wallet it was, I'd . . .
...... 5 If I broke something while shopping, I'd . . .
...... 6 You'll get sunburned if you . . .
...... 7 If you miss the bus, you . . .
...... 8 If you spoke Spanish, you . . .

a should try to find the owner.
b definitely return it.
c don't put on sunscreen.
d tell the manager.
e could work in South America.
f make you look great.
g got her hair styled.
h won't get to work on time.

2 Complete each unreal conditional sentence with the words in parentheses. Use the correct forms of the verbs.

1 If you .... pizza, I .... you eat it. (bring / help)
2 .... the job if it .... a lot of late nights? (you, accept / require)
3 If he .... you to go to the movies, ... with him? (ask / you, go out)
4 .... if you .... the lottery? (you do / win)
5 If she .... her ring in a public restroom, she .... anyone to return it. (leave, not expect)
6 If you .... my friend, I sure .... lonely. (not, be / be)
7 If I .... study, I .... biking on the new trails with you. (not, have to / go)
8 If the weather .... so chilly, we .... having fun at the beach today. (not, be / be)

UNIT 8 69

3 Rewrite the real conditional sentences in the unreal conditional. Use the true statements in parentheses to help you.

1 If he has time, he'll practice more. (He doesn't have time.)
....

2 If we go to Germany, I'll learn German. (We're not going to Germany.)
....

3 If she's late, she won't get a ticket to the concert. (She's never late.)
....

4 If I need to lose weight, I'll avoid carbs and sugars. (I don't need to lose weight.)
....

5 If we use this shampoo, our hair will look great. (We don't use this shampoo.)
....

4 Complete each present unreal conditional sentence. Use your own ideas.

1 If I went to my favorite store, ...
2 My family would be upset with me if ....
3 If I lived to be 100, ...
4 If I were an animal, ...

5 Write the correct phrases to complete each conversation. Use the words from the box. Not all of the words will be used.

| didn't see us   feel guilty   have a look   talk to the manager   the cashier |
| too much change   undercharged   would be wrong   would know |

1 **A:** Uh-oh. They gave us **(1)** ....
   B: Really? Let me **(2)** .... You're right.
   A: We should tell **(3)** ....
   B: But no one **(4)** ....
   A: I would know. If I kept the money, I'd **(5)** ....
   B: Actually, I would, too. Let's go back. It **(6)** .... to keep the money.

| I'd feel terrible   if I ate it   more than you ordered   should tell   to pay for it   What should I do |

2 **A:** Oh no. They gave you **(7)** ....
   B: You're right. I didn't order all this. **(8)** .... ?
   A: You **(9)** .... the waiter.
   B: But no one would know **(10)** ....
   A: True. But it would be wrong. And the waiter might have **(11)** ....
   B: Good point. **(12)** .... if that happened. I should tell him.
   A: I'm with you.

LESSON 3

1 Look at each picture. Complete the sentences with adjectives from the box.

| dishonest | disloyal | fair | honest | loyal | reliable | unfair | unreliable |

1 Hey! You got more peanuts than me. That's not .... It's so ....

2 Kendra is their friend, but they are excluding her. They are not .... friends. They're ....

3 He's cheating on the test. He's being .... It's disappointing that he's not ....

4 Dustin is late for work again. He's so .... He's not ....

2 Read about the people. How would you describe their character? Circle all the correct answers.

1 Tessa is a very firm boss. She expects everyone to be on time and to follow the rules. But she treats us all the same and she always stands up for her team members. For example, last week a customer started yelling at Rick. Tessa asked the customer not to speak to Rick in that way. Tessa is ....

   a loyal   b honest   c reliable   d fair   e unfair

2 When Jessica asked if she could borrow my car, she promised to take care of it. But she had a fender bender. She always damages my things. At least she didn't lie about it. She told me what happened and offered to pay for the repairs. I hope she keeps her promise this time! Jessica is ....

   a disloyal   b unreliable   c dishonest   d honest   e fair

3 I was disappointed recently to hear that a classmate was gossiping about me. She said I had taken something that didn't belong to me, but it wasn't true. My friend Adam stood up for me. He told everyone that the story wasn't true. He's a real friend. Adam is ....

   a dishonest   b fair   c unfair   d loyal   e dishonest

4 Jake found a pair of expensive sunglasses on a table in the coffee shop. He gave them to the manager and asked her to find the owner and return the sunglasses. I knew he would do the right thing. He always does. Jake is ....

   a dishonest   b unreliable   c honest   d loyal   e reliable

UNIT 8

LESSON 4

1 Read the article. What is it mainly about? Circle the correct answer.

a how being anonymous can negatively affect people's behavior online

b how to solve the problem of bad behavior online

c why the problem of anonymous bad behavior online is getting worse

BEHAVING BADLY ONLINE

The online environment lets people meet and talk with others around the world, play exciting games, and enjoy videos. Unfortunately, when identities are kept secret, there are opportunities to be mean, tell lies, and even steal—all with little chance of being punished. Research shows that people are more likely to behave badly when others don't know who they are, as is often the case online.

Psychologists believe that some parts of our personality don't change even when we are anonymous. Naturally kind people remain kind, but those who are naturally aggressive are free to reveal this ugly side, which they are forced to hide in society. Examples of this aggression are common in comments left below web articles, so much so that polite discussion often becomes impossible. Moreover, a study from the University of Wisconsin-Madison demonstrated that aggressive comments can negatively affect a reader's opinion of a topic. As a result, many online magazines have removed comments completely.

People also feel their identity is hidden when they download files illegally, an activity known as digital piracy. In daily life, few people would consider stealing due to the severe penalties. However, illegally downloading music, TV shows, and movies anonymously is extremely common, and punishment is rare. Various studies have shown that people consider digital piracy more acceptable than ordinary theft and that society doesn't view this crime as harshly. A survey of 2,000 university students showed that the participants were more likely to download files illegally if their friends weren't strongly against it.

Finally, the anonymous spreading of lies and false information on the Internet is a serious problem. In 2017, a large survey of experts asked if false information would be eliminated from the online environment over the next ten years. Of those surveyed, 49% believed the situation would improve thanks to technological advances and the natural human desire to work together to solve problems. However, 51% thought the situation would get worse because humans are willing to lie for money, success, and power, and new technologies will give them new ways to do so.

2 Reread the article in Exercise 1. Circle the correct words to complete each sentence.

1 When others don't know who we are, we are (**more** / less / just as) likely to behave badly.
2 Being anonymous (**doesn't change** / completely changes / partly changes) a person's personality.
3 Negative online comments (are good for discussions / **caused many online magazines to delete all comments** / have no effect on readers' opinions).
4 The author implies that digital piracy is common because (**people think it isn't such a bad crime** / it isn't really illegal / it's easy to do).
5 Slightly over half of the experts surveyed believed lies and false information on the Internet would (**get worse** / be eliminated / be about the same) in ten years.
6 One reason experts gave for lies and false information getting worse in ten years was that (people can't cooperate / technology won't advance in this area / **humans will lie to get what they want**).

3 Which paragraph best summarizes the article in Exercise 1? Circle the correct letter.

a People use the Internet for many purposes. Unfortunately, they often behave badly. It's important to avoid aggressive behavior even when anonymous. Furthermore, many people aren't strongly against digital piracy, so people do it. Most experts believe that lies and false information will disappear from the Internet in the future.

b Much bad behavior online occurs when identities are hidden. For example, naturally aggressive people will leave aggressive comments below web articles. Anonymous digital piracy is also very common because people don't view it as actual stealing. Slightly less than half of experts surveyed believe we can eliminate false information from the Internet in the future.

c When people are anonymous online, they often behave badly. However, there are a lot of naturally kind people who don't leave mean comments. Digital piracy is also very common, but it's really not that bad of a crime. A lot of experts think lies and false information will not be eliminated from the Internet in the future, but there's a good chance they will be.

GRAMMAR EXPANDER

1 Complete the sentences using the correct possessive nouns for the words in parentheses.
1. Whose phone is this? Is it ....? (Bart)
2. It's .... anniversary tomorrow. (Beth and Ted)
3. Whenever I travel for work, I borrow my .... luggage. (wife)
4. .... laptop is in my car. (Elis)
5. The .... TV is way bigger than ours. (Hendricks)
6. My .... leek soup is the best I've ever had. (sister)

2 Read the questions. Complete the answers using pronouns in place of the underlined nouns and noun phrases.
1. Did <u>Marco</u> break <u>the plate</u>? Yes, *he broke it*.
2. Did the homeless man keep the wallet he found? No, ...
3. Did a customer return <u>the coat</u> to <u>the couple</u> who dropped it? Yes, she ....
4. Did the server charge <u>June</u> for <u>the soup</u> she didn't like? No, he ....
5. Did your son tell you <u>both</u> about <u>his latest grades</u>? Yes, ...
6. Did <u>you</u> bring your <u>umbrella and coat</u>? Yes, ...

3 Complete the statements with <u>should</u>, <u>ought to</u>, and <u>had better</u> and your own ideas.
1. .... or your boss will be angry.
2. .... because it's never good to lie.
3. .... or someone else will have to pay for it.
4. Parents of teenagers ....
5. .... if you're in a hurry.
6. If your best friend is in trouble, ...

UNIT 8

4 Write the sentences with <u>must</u>, <u>have to</u>, and <u>be supposed to</u> and the words in parentheses.

1 (you / have / a ticket / to pass through the security checkpoint)
....

2 (you / not / use / a cell phone / in a hospital.)
....

3 (they / get / their car / inspected / before renewing / the registration)
....

4 (In / a library / everyone / speak quietly / and keep the noise down)
....

5 (we / not forget / to turn off the oven)
....

WRITING HANDBOOK

1 Read the conflicting ideas. Rewrite the sentences to use <u>on the other hand</u>, <u>even though</u>, <u>although</u>, and <u>however</u>.

1 I try to be an honest person. I sometimes lie to my friends.
   Even though / Although I try to be an honest person, I sometimes lie to my friends.

2 We don't have a lot of similar interests. We still like to hang out together.
....

3 Stella got a raise and can't wait to spend it. She's trying to save money for a car.
....

4 The new movie lost money. Reviews were very favorable.
....

5 It may have happened. It may not.
....

2 Read the situation. Write two paragraphs. In the first paragraph, explain why some people would decide to write the letter and why others would decide not to write it. In the second paragraph, describe what you would do. Use <u>on the one hand</u>, <u>on the other hand</u>, <u>even though</u>, <u>although</u>, and <u>however</u> to connect conflicting ideas.

> *This is a difficult situation. On the one hand, if you refuse to write the letter, you could damage your friendship. On the other hand, if you write the letter, you are being dishonest . . .*

Situation
A close friend is applying for a new job. He has not been working for six months and his family really needs the money. He asks you to write a recommendation letter. You value this person's friendship very much. But you know he is not a good match for the job. He is unreliable and not a good worker. Do you agree to write the letter?

UNIT 9 Enjoying the Arts

Warm-up

1 Look at each picture. Circle the correct style of art.

1 abstract / modern / traditional
2 realistic / abstract / digital 
3 handcrafted / traditional / modern 
4 traditional / digital / realistic 
5 modern / realistic / handcrafted 
6 abstract / handcrafted / traditional 

2 Complete the conversations with words from the box. You will not use all the words.

| abstract | digital | handcrafted | modern | realistic | traditional |

1 **Jeremy:** I love this painting of fresh baked breads. It looks so real. So delicious.
   Tabitha: I know! It's so detailed. I can almost smell the bread. ....

2 **Luis:** My sister visited Mexico recently. She brought back these beautiful blankets made by locals.
   Carla: Those are beautiful. The people there are so skilled. ....

3 **Trey:** That's some interesting artwork? Is it a painting?
   Julius: No. It was actually created on a computer. Isn't it amazing? ....

4 **Jayden:** Where did you get those amazing baskets?
   Derrick: From Uganda. They're made with the same types of tools and materials as they have been for years. ....

3 Match the phrase on the left with the reason for saying it on the right. Write the correct letter.

.... 1 Better yet, . . .   a to agree to a suggested action
.... 2 Tell you what . . .   b to introduce surprising information
.... 3 Speaking of which . . .   c to indicate you were just reminded of something
.... 4 Believe it or not . . .   d to introduce an offer to do something helpful
.... 5 In the meantime, . . .   e to increase the value of an offer
.... 6 It's a deal!   f to suggest an action to take before another one

LESSON 1

1 Read each sentence. Decide if it is in the active or passive voice. Write <u>A</u> or <u>P</u> on the line.

.... 1 My sister read a book on abstract paintings.
.... 2 The documentary on the subject was watched by many.
.... 3 My husband bought some folk art on his trip to Mexico.
.... 4 Scientists recently discovered new dinosaur fossils in Morocco.
.... 5 Many fossils were displayed by the curator at the museum exhibit.
.... 6 Some of his photographs have been purchased by local restaurants.

2 Use the information in the chart to write two sentences, one in the active voice and one in the passive voice. Use the verb in parentheses.

	Art Object	Artist	Year
1	*Vines and Olive Trees* (painting)	Joan Miró	1919
2	*Waterfront Demonstration* (photograph)	Dorothea Lange	1934
3	*Citizen Kane* (film)	Orson Welles	1941
4	*The Raven and the First Men* (wood figure)	Bill Reid	1994

1 (paint)
Active: .... *Joan Miró painted Vines and Olive Trees in 1919.* ....
Passive: .... *Vines and Olive Trees was painted by Joan Miró in 1919.* ....

2 (take)
Active: ....
Passive: ....

3 (direct)
Active: ....
Passive: ....

4 (create)
Active: ....
Passive: ....

3 Complete the conversation with sentences from the box. Not all of the sentences will be used.

> Never heard of her. Have you?   Not really. I'm not a big fan of modern art.
> Oh, I know her.   What? That's crazy.   Who's the artist?   Yes, definitely.

A: I love this sculpture, don't you?
B: **(1)** ....
A: Really? I think it's beautiful.
B: **(2)** ....

A: Let's see . . . Martina Fuller.
B: **(3)** ....
A: Actually, I haven't either. . . . Hey, check this out. Her sculpture sold for $10,000.
B: **(4)** ....

LESSON 2

1 Look at the pictures. Write the material.

1 a .... necklace
2 a .... bracelet
3 a .... bowl
4 a .... plate
5 a .... bag
6 a .... figure

2 Look at each group of objects. Which statements are true about all three objects? Circle the letters of all the correct answers.

1 a They are not made of wood.
   b They are (or were) used in the home for food or drink.
   c They are not made of stone.
   d They are examples of ceramic bowls.

2 a They are figures.
   b They are all glass.
   c They are made from different materials.
   d They are (or were) used in the home for food or drink.

3 a They are examples of necklaces.
   b They are examples of jewelry.
   c They are all metal.
   d They are made from different materials.

4 a They are carved from stone.
   b They are made of cloth.
   c They are not metal.
   d They are wood sculptures.

UNIT 9

3 Unscramble the words to write questions.

1 were / Where / made / those / leather chairs ? ....
2 made of / are / those / mugs / What ? ....
3 Were / painted / those / wood figures / by hand ? ....
4 was / designed / When / that / dress ? ....
5 this / manufactured / silver jewelry / Was / in Rhode Island ? ....
6 are / What / these / used for / cloth bags ? ....

4 Write a question to complete each conversation. Use the word in parentheses. Add a <u>wh-</u> question word if necessary. Use the passive voice.

1 A: *Where are these rugs woven* ? (these rugs / weave)
B: Those rugs? They come from Turkey.

2 A: ....? (this museum / build)
B: It was built in 1990.

3 A: ....? (these earrings / make)
B: The gold ones? They were made in Dubai.

4 A: ....? (that bowl / make / of)
B: That's polished wood. The same person made these plates.

5 A: ....? (those fabrics / dye)
B: It's all done by hand, using dyes made from local plants.

6 A: ....? (this pitcher / paint / by local artist)
B: Yes, it was. A local artist paints many pieces in our shop.

7 A: ....? (these stone figures / use / for)
B: They were used for meditation practices.

5 Write the sentences in the correct order to make a conversation. Use the sentences in the box. Not all of the sentences will be used.

I love those bowls. Where were they made?	Oh, those were made in Thailand.
I'm not a big fan of handcrafted items.	Really? They're very nice. Can I take a closer look?
No, the metal ones.	The wood ones?
Of course. Let me get them for you.	Was that pitcher made in Japan?

A: (1) ....
B (2) ....
A: (3) ....
B: (4) ....
A: (5) ....
B: (6) ....

LESSON 3

1 Complete the statements with the correct phrases from the box.

| fascinated by | influenced by | inspired by | moved by |

1. His photos of baby animals and their mothers in nature are so touching. Everyone who sees them is sure to be .... his images.
2. I have always been .... abstract art. I am especially drawn to Helen Frankenthaler's painting *Beach*.
3. Frankenthaler was .... the work of artists such as Jackson Pollock and Franz Kline. However, she developed her own distinct approach to the abstract style.
4. Many artists are .... their peers who introduce them to new methods or new ways of looking at their materials and their subjects. This often allows them to grow as artists.

2 Complete the sentences. Circle the correct answer.

1. My aunt was an amazing macramé crafter. Her walls were covered with beautiful pieces woven entirely by her hand. I now make macramé plant hangers. I believe my style was very much (**influenced** / moved / fascinated) by my aunt.
2. I find mixed media journaling to be very intriguing. Although some people describe this type of art as nothing special, I am (inspired / **fascinated** / moved) by the combination of text and imagery and multiple materials.
3. The movie we watched last night was so sad. I must have cried at least three times. I think my whole family was (influenced / **moved** / inspired) by it.
4. Stella has always been (moved / influenced / **inspired**) by her father's persistence in finding time to paint each day, despite his extremely busy work schedule.

3 Complete the biography of Pablo Picasso. Write passive participial phrases with the words in parentheses.

Pablo Ruiz Picasso began studying art with his father. Then from 1895 until 1904, he painted in Barcelona. During this time, he made his first trip to Paris, where he **(1)** .... (inspire) the artwork of Henri de Toulouse-Lautrec. In Paris, Picasso **(2)** .... (influence) all the poverty he saw. He was sad and angry that so many people lived without enough food or clothing. He painted many pictures of poor people to bring attention to their situation.

In 1906, Picasso met the artist Henri Matisse, who was to become his longtime friend. Picasso was interested in Matisse's style, but he did not imitate it. The artists he really admired were Georges Braque and Joan Miró. Picasso **(3)** .... (fascinate) Braque's and Miró's work. Together the three artists started the movement known as Cubism.

One of Picasso's most famous artistic pieces is *Guernica*. Picasso **(4)** .... (move) the violence of the Spanish Civil War. This prompted him to paint the piece.

UNIT 9

LESSON 4

1 Read the article. What kind of reader is the article for? Circle the best answer.

a a beginning artist who wants to get better

b a professional artist who has a lot of natural talent

c an art teacher who wants students to stop making mistakes

Nurturing Your Artistic Talent

1. So, you'd like to improve your artistic ability, but you think you don't have any natural talent? The truth is you don't have to be born with talent to be a good artist—and to enjoy making art. Artistic skill can be learned.

2. Many people who try painting get frustrated and give up because they feel they lack the "artistic gene." However, the real problem is that they have just never been trained to look at the world like an artist. When non-artists look at the subject of a drawing, they see it with the left side of their brains. They immediately begin figuring out the meaning of what they see. An artist pays attention to what is actually being seen—the lines. Are they straight or curved? Dark or light? Where do they intersect?

3. Want to learn to see like an artist? Try this exercise. Find a large photo of a face and try to draw it. It's OK if your drawing looks bad. Then turn the photo upside down and try again. This time focus only on the relationships of the intersecting lines and shapes. Almost always, the upside-down drawing, when turned right side up, will be much better than the right-side-up version! How did this happen? By turning the photo upside down, the left side of your brain stopped looking at the photo as a face. Instead, the right side of your brain took over and began seeing the photo in a new way.

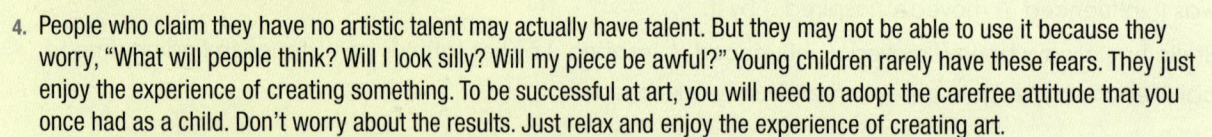

4. People who claim they have no artistic talent may actually have talent. But they may not be able to use it because they worry, "What will people think? Will I look silly? Will my piece be awful?" Young children rarely have these fears. They just enjoy the experience of creating something. To be successful at art, you will need to adopt the carefree attitude that you once had as a child. Don't worry about the results. Just relax and enjoy the experience of creating art.

5. Anyone can develop the necessary skills and understanding to create art. Those with natural talent are able to learn more quickly and easily, but even they will need training, practice, and hard work. So, stop making excuses and get started! Take art lessons, read books on art, and attend art exhibits. Expose yourself to a variety of techniques, kinds of art, and other artists. And think of becoming an artist as a lifetime journey. Stop worrying about making mistakes and enjoy the adventure!

2 Read the article in Exercise 1 again. Answer the questions. Circle the letter.

1 What is the main idea of paragraph 2?

a Lacking the "artistic gene" is a real problem.

b You should always draw faces upside down.

c It's important to learn to see like an artist.

2 What is the main idea of paragraph 4?

a Children are better artists than adults.

b Fear of making mistakes prevents many adults from creating art.

c Beginners' artwork is usually silly.

3 What is the main idea of paragraph 5?

a Artists with natural talent don't have to work hard.

b It takes a very long time to become a good artist.

c Anyone can make art with practice and hard work.

3 Read the quotations by famous artists. Find a paragraph in the article in Exercise 1 that presents an opinion similar to that expressed by each artist. Write the number of the paragraph on the line.

.... 1 "I am doubtful of any talent, so whatever I choose to be will be accomplished only by long study and work." —Jackson Pollock

.... 2 "Creation begins with vision. The artist has to look at everything as though seeing it for the first time." —Henri Matisse

.... 3 "Every child is an artist. The problem is how to remain an artist once we grow up." —Pablo Picasso

4 Read the third paragraph of the article in Exercise 1 again. Try the drawing exercise on a separate sheet of paper. Then answer the questions.

1 Which drawing was easier? ....
2 Which drawing took more time? ....
3 Which drawing looks more like the photograph? ....
4 Did the exercise help you to see more like an artist? Explain. ....

GRAMMAR EXPANDER

1 If possible, rewrite the sentences, changing the active voice to the passive voice. If a sentence cannot be changed to the passive voice, circle the verb and write <u>intransitive</u> on the line.

1 In Florence, we walked to the Accademia Gallery to see Michelangelo's *David*.
....

2 Donna Karan will show her spring collection at New York Fashion Week.
....

3 A new exhibit of surrealist paintings arrives at our museum this fall.
....

4 Those landscape paintings seem quite dark and depressing.
....

5 Paul Klee used simple stick figures, eyes, arrows, and quilts of color in his many paintings.
....

6 Michelangelo painted *The Creation of Adam* in 1508.
....

DID YOU KNOW . . . ?
The highest known price paid for a painting was set in 2017, when *Salvator Mundi* by Leonardo da Vinci sold for $450.4 million dollars!

2 Choose the best answer to complete each sentence. Circle the letter.

1 We probably .... invited to the wedding. They plan to only invite close family.
   a won't be   b weren't being   c haven't been   d weren't

2 The photography exhibit .... attended by over 2,000 people so far.
   a was   b has been   c is going to be   d is being

3 This serving tray .... made in 1569.
   a is   b has been   c was being   d was

4 Earlier today, visitors .... taking pictures in the museum.
   a have   b were   c will be   d have been

5 Right now, connections .... made at the convention.
   a were   b were being   c are being   d have been

3 Use the words to write sentences in the passive voice.

1 (Your laptop / repair / now)
   ....

2 (Many products / make / in China)
   ....

3 (The Guggenheim Museum / in New York / build / in 1959)
   ....

4 ("Under Pressure" / write / by David Bowie)
   ....

5 (French / speak / in Quebec, Canada)
   ....

6 (A new theater / open / next year)
   ....

4 Rewrite the sentences in the passive voice. Use a <u>by</u> phrase only if it is important or necessary to know who or what is performing the action.

1 Artists hand-painted these bowls in France.
   ....

2 Gucci is showing a lot of bright colors this season.
   ....

3 Stores everywhere are going to sell her sterling silver bracelets.
   ....

4 People in Guatemala carved these wood figures.
   ....

5 Swiss companies still make the world's best watches.
   ....

6 Shakespeare wrote *The Tempest*.
   ....

5 Rewrite the passive voice sentences in Exercise 4 as <u>yes</u> / <u>no</u> questions.

1. *Are these bowls hand-painted in France?*
2.
3.
4.
5.
6.

WRITING HANDBOOK

1 Read the paragraph. Underline the topic sentence. Circle the supporting details. Cross out the two sentences that don't belong.

> I have been to museums in countries all over the world, but my favorite painting is in a museum close to my home. I am a real fan of *The Master's Bedroom* by Andrew Wyeth because I find it very peaceful. Andrew Wyeth died in 2009 at the age of 91. The painting shows a dog curled up on a bed, taking an afternoon nap. Sunlight is coming in through the window and warming the dog. The painting makes me feel relaxed because the dog and the bed look so comfortable. The bedroom is very simple, and the colors in the painting are soft and neutral, making the scene seem really calm. Wyeth's most famous painting is *Christina's World,* which is at the Museum of Modern Art in New York City.

2 Write a paragraph about a piece of art or a handcrafted object that inspires you. It can be famous or something you own. Create a topic sentence that states the most important thing you want to say about it. Then write five detail sentences that each support your topic sentence.

I own a silver bracelet that is very special to me. It was given to me by my father when I was a teenager. He bought it in a handicraft market in Kenya . . .

Ideas
painting   figure
sculpture pitcher
drawing   bowl
photography necklace
plate   earrings
bracelet

UNIT 9

UNIT 10 Technology

Warm-up

1 Read each situation. What problem is the person having with a device? Circle the correct answer.

1 Last night, I downloaded a file that I though my friend sent me. Now there's something wrong with my computer. I can't open any folders and my screen keeps going black.
   a There's no Wi-Fi connection
   b There's a virus.
   c The battery's dead.

2 I forgot to charge my phone last night. Now I can't get it to turn on.
   a The battery's dead.
   b It's overheating.
   c It's running slowly.

3 I can't do anything on my laptop. The mouse won't move. Everything seems to be stuck.
   a The screen is frozen.
   b The file didn't save.
   c It's overheating.

4 Hello? Hello? I can't hear you. Can you hear me?
   a There's a virus.
   b The battery's dead.
   c There's no sound.

5 What happened? I definitely remember making those changes to the file yesterday. Now I can't find them.
   a The battery's dead.
   b The file didn't save.
   c The screen is frozen.

2 Complete the paragraph with phrases from the box.

battery was dead	no sound	running so slowly
files didn't save	no Wi-Fi connection	was overheating
might have a virus	screen was frozen	

Yesterday was a day of non-stop technology trouble. I was at the airport when I got a text to get on a video call with a client. There was **(1)** .... where I was sitting, so I couldn't get online. I raced around looking for somewhere to connect! Of course, then, my laptop seemed to take forever to turn on. Everything was **(2)** .... ! When I finally got on the call, there was **(3)** .... at all! My speakers were broken. Thankfully, I had some headphones. But in the middle of the call, the video stopped working. The **(4)** .... It was stuck. I turned the laptop off and texted the client and my boss from my phone to explain what happened. They were both very understanding. The client asked me to email him some important files. But when I got back on my laptop, I couldn't find them anywhere! I thought I **(5)** .... , so I ran my anti-virus app. But the laptop was clean. That's when I realized that the **(6)** .... the last time I worked on them. The updated versions were gone! What's more, the laptop was getting very hot. It **(7)** .... Finally, the laptop just turned off on its own. The **(8)** .... even though I had charged it that morning. It was so frustrating. It's definitely time for a new laptop!

3 Match the statements with a similar meaning. Write the correct letter.

..... 1 I don't get it.
..... 2 Don't jump to conclusions.
..... 3 What a pain in the neck.
..... 4 Better safe than sorry.
..... 5 It gives you peace of mind.

a It's so annoying.
b Better to be careful now and avoid later problems.
c You can be free from worry.
d I don't understand.
e Don't assume something before you know for sure.

LESSON 1

1 Read about people's problems with devices. What should they do? Circle all the possible solutions.

1 Christine's laptop is running very slowly.
   a Check the volume.
   b Restart the router.
   c Run a virus scan.
   d Make sure the cables are plugged in.
   e Delete her browsing history.

2 Nathan can't hear what other people are saying on a group call. They can't hear him either.
   a Move closer to the hotspot.
   b Check the volume.
   c Delete his browsing history.
   d Make sure he's not on mute.
   e Try restarting.

3 Jill's screen is frozen. She can't open or close any windows.
   a Try restarting.
   b Run a virus scan.
   c Restart the router.
   d Move closer to the hotspot.
   e Make sure she's not on mute.

2 Complete the conversations with words from the box.

| browsing history | on mute | plugged in | router | virus scan | volume |

1 **A:** Online Support. Can I help you?
  B: Yes. I'm trying to listen to a movie on my laptop, but there's no sound. Can you help me?
  A: Sure. First, make sure your .... is turned up. Check the speakers.
  B: Let's see . . . Yes, they're fine.
  A: OK. Next, check to see if you are .... You'll see a red line over your speaker indicator.
  B: Oh, wow! You're right. I didn't realize that had happened. It works now. Thank you.

2 **A:** Online Support, how may I help you?
  B: My computer is running very slowly. What should I do?
  A: Try deleting the .... That often helps.
  B: I've done that. And I've restarted. It's still very slow.
  A: OK, let me see. It might be a virus. Have you run a .... ?
  B: No, I haven't. I'll do that now.

UNIT 10   85

3 Match each action with the correct purpose. Write the letter on the line.

..... 1 She deleted her browsing history because she ...
..... 2 I enrolled in an electronics course because I ...
..... 3 They downloaded a GPS app because they ...
..... 4 Breanna bought a better headset because she ...
..... 5 Adam started using the Wunderlist app because he ...

a needed to get accurate directions for their trip.
b wanted to listen to music on the computer.
c wanted to speed up her laptop.
d needed to be more organized.
e wanted to learn how to repair computers.

4 Rewrite the sentences in Exercise 3 using infinitives of purpose.

1 ....
2 ....
3 ....
4 ....
5 ....

5 Answer each Why question with an infinitive of purpose. Use the words in parentheses.

1 **A:** Why are you signing up for that service?
   B: .... (videos / stream)
2 **A:** Why did you delete that program?
   B: .... (my phone / speed up)
3 **A:** Why did you shop for a new monitor online?
   B: .... (time / save)
4 **A:** Why should I upgrade my storage system?
   B: .... (more storage / get)
5 **A:** Why should he call the Tech Guys?
   B: .... (with / his computer / get help)

6 Complete the conversation with words from the box. Not all the phrases will be used.

| a minute | a virus scan | browser history | my tablet | take care |
| to start | very quickly | very slowly | volume | worth a try |

A: Hey, Grace. Got **(1)** .... ? I have a problem with **(2)** ....
B: Sure! What's wrong?
A: Well, it's running **(3)** ....
B: Have you tried deleting the **(4)** .... ?
A: Sounds like a good place **(5)** ....
B: Well, it's **(6)** .... And if that doesn't work, you should run **(7)** ....
A: Thanks! I'll do that.

7 Write about a time you had trouble with a device. How did you troubleshoot the problem? What was the solution?

LESSON 2

1 Match the computer systems and software on the left with the definitions on the right. Write the correct letter.

.... 1 an Internet browser
.... 2 an e-mail account
.... 3 an online backup service
.... 4 a streaming service
.... 5 a password manager
.... 6 a cloud storage service
.... 7 an application
.... 8 an anti-virus program

a an application that creates and saves your passwords
b a computer program that allows you to do specific tasks
c a service used to manage your electronic messages
d an online service you can use to listen to music or watch movies whenever you want to
e an application that runs on a computer to find and remove viruses
f an application you use for accessing information online
g a service that helps you save space on your computer by storing files online instead of on your computer
h a service that protects files from being lost by automatically saving a copy online

2 Complete the sentences with words from the box.

| anti-virus | applications | cloud storage service | email account | internet browser |
| online backup service | password manager | streaming service | | |

1 I use an .... to automatically save copies of all of my documents. This way I don't forget to save while I work, and I'll never lose a file.
2 My sister has used the same .... for more than 25 years. I guess having the same e-mail address for all these years allows her to stay in touch with a lot more people from her past.
3 I want to start watching movies on demand, but I can't decide which .... to use. There are so many options with different price ranges and download speeds.
4 My brother is an IT guy. He says that Google Chrome is the best .... Compared to some of the other options, it provides a simpler and faster way of accessing the Internet.
5 Syreesa has way too many photos on her laptop. It's causing problems because she doesn't have enough space. Her uncle suggested that she move her photos to a ....
6 It's impossible to remember all the passwords I have for all the sites I visit. I'm looking for a good .... if you have any recommendations.
7 It seems that his computer has a virus. He should run a scan on it with an .... program.

3 Look at the chart comparing two laptop computers. Complete the sentences, using (not) as . . . as and the adjectives. Use the adverbs almost, quite, just, and nearly.

	Ace EC650u laptop	Simsun B400 laptop
Price	$619	$599
Weight	5 pounds / 2.3 kilograms	3 pounds / 1.4 kilograms
Screen size	16 inches / 40.6 centimeters	15.5 inches / 39.4 centimeters
Screen quality	◐	◐
Touchpad ease of use	●	◐
Speed	●	◐
Speaker quality	●	●
Noise	◐	●

KEY
Better ●
↑
◐
↓
Worse ○

1 The quality of the Ace screen is ......just as good as...... (good) the quality of the Simsun screen.
2 The Simsun screen isn't .... (large) the Ace screen.
3 The Simsun laptop is .... (fast) the Ace laptop.
4 The Ace laptop isn't .... (light) the Simsun laptop.
5 The Simsun laptop is .... (expensive) the Ace laptop.
6 The Simsun touchpad isn't .... (easy to use) the Ace touchpad.

4 Which laptop in Exercise 3 would you buy? Explain your reasons, using (not) as . . . as and some of the adverbs from Exercise 3.

5 Make a conversation using sentences from the box. Not all the sentences will be used.

Do you have a particular one in mind?
I think it's about time we tried a new streaming service.
It's just as secure as our old system.
It's not as quick as some of the other ones out there.
She's always up on the latest stuff.

Suppose we ask my friend Gloria for advice.
Suppose we get a new password manager.
Well, I've heard that Cinema II is pretty fast.
What's wrong with the one we have?

A: (1)
B: (2)
A: (3)
B: (4)
A: (5)
B: (6)
    (7)

88 UNIT 10

LESSON 3

1 Read about why the people are using the Internet. Then match each person to a reason. Write the correct number.

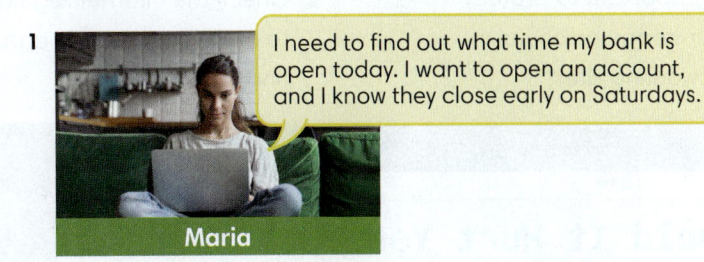

1. Maria: I need to find out what time my bank is open today. I want to open an account, and I know they close early on Saturdays.

2. Joe: I bought a digital subscription to my daily newspaper.

3. David and Elaine: We can get the best travel deals online.

4. Alexa: I can get in touch with my friends or family anytime.

5. Bryan: Job opportunities are right at my fingertips.

.... a to book travel services
.... b to find information
.... c for job hunting
.... d for instant messaging
.... e to read my favorite blogs, newspapers, and magazines

2 Write three sentences to describe your own Internet use. What do you do often? What do you rarely do?

DID YOU KNOW...?
The average person spends 6 hours and 42 minutes online each day. Logging in just over ten hours a day, people in the Philippines spend the most time online. The Japanese spend the least time connected: just three hours and forty-five minutes.

UNIT 10

LESSON 4

1 Read the article from a career advice website. What is the main idea of the article? Circle the correct letter.

a It's a good idea to use social media to help in your job search.

b It's important to protect your image on social networking sites.

c Check the Internet regularly to make sure people can find you.

Social Networking: Could It Hurt Your Job Search?

To be the best candidate for a job, you'll need more than an impressive résumé and a nice suit. You also need to make sure there isn't any information about you online that could cause an employer not to hire you. A recent study found that 77 percent of recruiters search the Internet for information about applicants they are considering for a job. Thirty-five percent of these same recruiters say they have rejected an applicant based on information they have found online.

"A profile on a social networking site can show you a lot more of a person's character than a résumé," says Jen Romney, a corporate recruiter who recently began looking up the names of applicants on the Web. "It's surprising what you can find. I once had to make a difficult decision between two excellent applicants. When I found one of the applicants' profile on a social networking site, the decision became much easier. The man's profile was full of negative comments about his job and boss. In one post he wrote, 'I'm calling in sick today—because I'm sick of work!' I don't need to tell you that he didn't get the job."

Romney warns that as people share more of their lives online, it becomes harder to keep one's private life completely private. "Everything is public," says Romney. "It's called the World Wide Web for a reason. Anyone in the world can see it."

While not all employers research potential employees online, it's worth being a little careful to make sure that social networking doesn't ruin your career opportunities. You can protect yourself by following four simple rules:

1. Think before you click. Before you post photos of you and your friends partying or comments about how you hate your job, ask yourself: Would I be comfortable talking about this in a job interview?

2. Take control. Most social networking sites have privacy controls. Take the time to figure them out and use them wisely. Set your controls so that only people you've chosen as "friends" can view your profile and post messages on your page.

3. Review. Check your profile regularly to see what has been posted. Type your name and e-mail address into a search engine to see what is on the Internet about you.

4. Delete. Remove any potentially embarrassing or offensive posts, information, or photos. Ask friends to delete anything inappropriate about you on their own profiles.

2 Look at the underlined words in the article in Exercise 1. Use the context to match the terms with their meanings. Write the letter.

.... 1 recruiter
.... 2 search engine
.... 3 profile
.... 4 post
.... 5 private

a only for a particular group to see, not for everyone
b information, photos, comments, etc. put on a website
c a person who finds candidates to fill job openings
d page on a social networking site with a member's personal information
e a program that helps you find things on the Internet

3 Answer the questions according to the information in the article in Exercise 1.

1 How does the Internet make it easier for employers to get information about job applicants?

....

2 What type of information in an online profile can hurt a job applicant's chances of getting a job?

....

4 Do you think the article in Exercise 1 gives good advice? What have you done, or what do you plan to do, to protect your image online? Explain your answer.

GRAMMAR EXPANDER

1 Read the conversation. Underline all the infinitives that express a purpose.

A: It's 6:00. Are you going home?
B: No, I'm staying late to finish the agenda for tomorrow's meeting. How about you?
A: I'm leaving now. I'm going to stop at Ernie's Electronics to buy a new printer. Then I'm going to ComputerWorld to get something else on sale.
B: Really? What?
A: I'm thinking about getting myself a tablet.
B: What's wrong with your laptop at home?
A: Nothing. But the kids use it to surf the Internet all the time.
B: What do they do online?
A: Lots of stuff. They use the laptop to check e-mail, download music, chat with their friends, and play games.

2 Complete the sentences with your own information. Use an infinitive of purpose or <u>for</u>.

1 I wish I could find a streaming service ....
2 I need a new phone app ....
3 I'd like to find some software ....
4 I use my Smart TV ....
5 I usually shop online ....

3 Complete each sentence with the correct form of the adjective or adverb in parentheses.

1 Of the three cameras we looked at, this one is the .... to use. (hard)
2 My new monitor still isn't big enough. I need something even .... (big)
3 I'm trying to save money. What is the .... storage system available? (expensive)
4 I can't stop laughing. This is the .... movie I've seen in a while. (funny)
5 Paul's sketches are amazing. His animation work is just as .... (impressive)
6 Of all the printers at work, the one in the conference room is the .... (reliable)
7 I shop online for most of my clothes. It's much .... than going to a store. (easy)
8 We've never had a .... vacation than this one. It was so much fun! (exciting)

4 Rewrite the sentences. Make a comparison using an adverb.

1. The X-2 printer and the Workzone printer are both a little loud. The Lazerfine printer is extremely loud.
   The Lazerfine printer prints much more loudly than the X-2 and the Workzone printers.

2. Elisa's laptop is fairly efficient. My laptop operates very efficiently.
   ....

3. His new game is easy to play. Her old game is a lot easier to play.
   ....

4. My Internet at home is extremely slow. The Internet at the office is somewhat slow.
   ....

5. Before the accident, he didn't drive very carefully. Since the accident, he is more careful.
   ....

6. The ABC monitor is large. The XYZ monitor is excessive in size.
   ....

WRITING HANDBOOK

Write three paragraphs about a piece of computer software or a service that you use. In the first paragraph, write about the upside of using it. In the second, write about the downside. In the third paragraph, state whether or not you recommend it to others.

NetMovie is the most popular movie streaming service. There are a lot of benefits to being a member. First of all, it offers more movies than the other companies . . .

Ideas
music/movie streaming service
Internet browser
photo/video editing software
anti-virus program
email service
password manager
presentation application
cloud storage service

UNIT 10